The Outcome

by David Douglass Light and Scott Messer

A novel approach to selling.

Good Selling!

Sales Evolution, LLC

Broomall, Pennsylvannia

The Outcome is a work of fiction. Names, characters, places, and incidents are either the product of the author's imagination or are used fictitiously. Any resemblance to actual persons (living or dead), business establishments, events, or locales is entirely coincidental.

The Outcome
by David Douglass Light and Scott Messer

On-Demand Printed Edition, published August 2012
ISBN: 978-0-9857456-0-8

Sales Evolution, LLC
2837 Dogwood Lane
Broomall, PA 19008
(610) 353-8686

www.SalesEvolution.com

ACKNOWLEDGEMENTS

I want to thank Gerri, Holly, and David, and my sisters Cate and Dee for their support. I wish to acknowledge my appreciation to Scott Messer, who personifies the central message of the story: That all human achievement starts with a truthful conversation about creating an outcome, and about eliminating the uncertainty of reaching a goal. That is exactly how this book started one year ago at the Cracker Barrel Restaurant in Plymouth Meeting, Penn. I also want to thank him for his wisdom, support, and unfailing friendship.

My sincere appreciation also to our editor and designer John Donica, whose talent, creativeness, and sense of humor effectively neutralized those malicious forces of uncertainty that were hell-bent on exploiting my debilitating distaste for detail.

› *David Douglass Light*

Thanks to my wife Evelyn and daughter Hannah for all their support, to Dave Light for his creative genius and wonderful story-telling abilities, and to sales professionals everywhere who understand how to have a conversation that leads their prospect

The Outcome

to self-discover the true personal outcome the prospect wishes to accomplish. You have a hard job. We trust THE OUTCOME makes it easier.

> › *Scott Messer*

INTRODUCTION

O N MY SON'S 11TH BIRTHDAY, I bought him a portable computerized chess board. I couldn't play chess worth a lick, but David was a natural and I thought he would benefit from regular sessions of challenging play, even if meant using a coupon at Radio Shack to purchase a stand-in for the old man. That evening I assembled it, and I couldn't resist sparing a round with the board with a depressingly predictable outcome, even though I had set the competition level to a mere 3 out of 10. I also quickly discovered that the game came packaged with a personality. The programmer, no doubt some nerd who can't talk to girls, had included a sub-routine that evaluated the opponent's pattern of play. A bad move triggered any one of a library of obnoxiously critical admonitions. They barked out through a small speaker, which also served as the penalty buzzer if one attempted an illegal move — a real board-rattler that punctuated many of my "fat-fingered" missteps. When it detected either a particularly clueless rookie move or a doomed series of moves, the electronic voice would let rip with an irritating android heckle, which drove me to distraction during my first round until I finally read the instructions on how to shut the thing up.

Determined not to surrender to the machine, I bought a book
by chess master Gary Kasparov, and after studying it for a
few hours confidently took up the board again, voice and all.
Using the "Queen's Gambit" opening, I confidently cranked
up the competition level to 5, and drilled in with a restored
Russian-inspired rigor. My first move went unchallenged by the
device. But with my second move the computer launched into an
obnoxious taunt:

> *"You must be a salesman! Only a salesman would make a
> move like that!"*

I was mortified. I slammed the book on the table, infuriated at the
insult from the machine. First, on general principles, I thought,
"Why would RadioShack sell a game that insulted salespeople?
After all, their stores are staffed with commissioned salespeople!"
But what drove me to toss the entire set into the garbage can was
that the machine was correct! I was, in fact, a salesman! Not
only had the damn device beaten and insulted me, it had read my
style of play and was able to decipher something about my career
choice. I was devastated! Naturally, after retrieving the game from
the trash, I discovered that the board fired off the same salesman
insult regardless of who made a particularly bad opening salvo.
But the pure chauvinism of the statement made me feel even worse,
because it reinforced the stereotype: Anyone who is a salesman
is some kind of idiot who isn't capable of fielding a decent chess
opening. The whole ordeal immediately invoked Willie Loman
in "Death Of A Salesman," plus a round of the sort of existential
spelunking that I had girded myself against over my entire career.

Selling is difficult and disciplined work that requires bullet-proof self-esteem and supreme self-confidence. But Radio Shack had managed to shatter my defenses with some cheap silicon and a $49 box of magnetic plastic pawns.

Fortunately, salespeople have nothing if not selective memory. Fast forward a few years and I am a CEO attending a Sales & Marketing Executives International (SMEI) meeting lead by the Chapter President, Scott Messer, founder of Sales Evolution. Scott was giving a presentation titled "Stop Qualifying You For Them. Start Qualifying Them For You!"

He also spoke about what he termed the "Salesperson's Bill of Rights," which dictate certain rules of engagement that salespeople are entitled to, and had the right expect and enforce. The "Dominant D" in me immediately resonated with those two pillars of Scott's "Guess-Free Selling"™ methodology. The Sales Evolution approach was 180 degrees out of phase with everything I'd been hearing in sales training for 20 years. As a start-up CEO, I was itching for new directions in every aspect of my business. I was tethered to sales and business development, along with the core management, finance, and P&L duties. But as an inveterate sales guy, every innovation that served organizational objectives had to, at the same time, serve sales. At that particular time, I was struggling with the sales team on a truly immense piece of business, and I was eager for a new approach that would move the ball forward. During our brief conversation following his presentation, Scott asked me two questions that convinced me that I had found that new approach:

Scott: "So Dave, do you like being sold to?"

Dave: "No."

Scott: "Do you like being closed?"

Dave: "No."

Scott: "Well then, what makes you think that your prospects like being sold to and closed?"

I had no answer to that last question, even though I understood intuitively that prospects hated it. So, I hired him.

"But if they hate it, why don't they tell me they hate it?" That was just one of the many naive questions I asked myself over the course of the coming weeks and months as Scott took me through Sales Evolution's Guess-Free Selling training classes and coaching calls.

As human beings, we understand that our motives are inherently self-serving, even when our good works are directed toward others. This book is a business novel which, at its heart, is about acknowledging this fundamental truth in a business-affirming way, as it applies to an essential human activity: Selling stuff.

Outcome Decision-Making and The Certainty Principle propose that the core reason behind any action-creating motive resolves itself into the outcome that the individual expects at the end of the action or course of actions, and the uncertainties related to making it happen. These two features define the complete conundrum of the human enterprise. Pair Benjamin Disraeli's: "We all live under the same sky, but we do not all have the same horizons," with Franklin Delano Roosevelt's: "We have nothing to fear but fear itself." There you have the essence of human aspiration: Outcome and uncertainty.

If we presume that no important human achievement can be achieved alone, then the next logical question is, "How do I optimize the likelihood that the outcomes I wish to achieve will become reality?" Certainly one tried-and-true method is to muster support from every possible sector. In business, this means finding people who are specialized, schooled, drilled, and motivated in the processes of moving business forward, of capitalizing on commercial opportunities, and of creating low-risk paths to the outcome they seek to achieve. In a phrase, find Sales Professionals. Salespeople are the change agents of the business world. They concentrate on developing the core skill of assuring that those who seek a specific outcome will achieve it through the goods and services that they provide. The process requires high certainty and confidence, and low risk to get it done in as little time and with as little friction as possible.

But as evidenced by the digital chess board's "salesman" scolding, the reputation of sales and sales people is hardly unblemished when it comes to creating certainty in the minds of prospects. The negative stereotypes are there because seemingly everyone has a story about a bad experience with a salesperson. "The Outcome" presents a positive counter-story to this negative stereotype. It presents sales professionals as deal makers who play an essential role in the world's economy. It depicts the real-life wheeling and dealing — even tragedy — that salespeople struggle with in placing even the most basic food items into a grocery store freezer case.

I admit that this unvarnished sales story presents some uncomfortable truths about what makes things tick in world of global commerce, but we are reminded daily of the excesses that competition and expedience bring to every area of human endeavor, inside and outside of the business arena. Integrity under fire is not the exclusive domain of commerce. "The Outcome" is an authentic one-woman morality play — a narrative tale that contrasts the dark intellectual and ethical business challenges against one person's commitment to the truth. Jane Dreyfus, in her instinct to do the only right thing, is drawn into an important transformation in her philosophy and her business methodology as she learns that there is another way, the "Guess-Free" way.

Many readers have asked me whether or not the story is real. I will say that I did fabricate the characters and events, however, it naturally laces together real events and experiences I have had over the course of my career. All of the business elements of the story are based in the reality of the global seafood business, as well as other industries engaged in the global dynamics of shifting markets and sources of supply. People often question whether there is really a significant level of corruption and skullduggery in business, and I say this, without a deep breath or condemnation about it: "Yes," though probably less today than in earlier times because of increased business transparency. For those who are on the periphery of business, and are not familiar with the risks and shortfalls attendant to every business endeavor, perhaps it will come as a surprise that, for the most part, there are very few businesses, great or small, that did not begin with a little sleight-of-hand, persuasion, a confidence game, or out-and-out corruption by some scoundrel, manipulator, or robber baron. Having said that, where would we be without them? It is left to the rest of us to walk Buddha's middle path where we neither stray from the straight and narrow nor tell a lie. Save for those promoters who have been able to tread the thin line of propriety, we would probably all be living in the dark ages and speaking Aramaic.

This book is not precisely about the world of the entrepreneurship and the various devices implemented to create enterprise. That's a tale for another day. No, this book is about civilization's essential need for salespeople. This is the story of one of them. The premise of "The Outcome" is that over the past few decades the necessity for a well-trained, coherent, and aligned sales force has been shown to be essential for the execution of any realistic business plan. To go farther in the new global-digital millennium, an entirely new form of salesmanship — one we choose to call Guess-Free Selling — has emerged. It's basis is the one element that guarantees to drive business resolutely forward, for better or for worse. Simply, the truth. No assumptions, no assertions, no guessing. Just the truth as the prospective customer perceives it. In a world where all information and all products are essentially free, it is a process that provides salespeople with the skills to dutifully and expediently fulfill their professional responsibility as enablers of the outcome that the prospect is truly seeking to achieve.

> *David Douglass Light*

The Outcome

CHAPTER 1

Jane Dreyfus loves sales.

So what if he married Marilyn Monroe? Arthur Miller was an idiot! Why award a Pulitzer to a guy for taking a potshot at the soul of the American enterprise? Of global enterprise? "Death of a Salesman" . . . What the hell did a playwright know about selling? About enabling innovation? About changing the world?!

Jane loves that fact that selling has brought her fortunes — and has broken her. The experience of deal-making has taught her much about humanity, and shown her much of the planet it calls home. She loves that sales has made her both indomitable and, at times, dishonorable. That it has taught her pride and humility. Sales people are the energizers and the enablers of the business world. They make change happen. The ambition and the psychology of it all fascinates her. Her heroes are grand-standing, world-class sales people. From Amelia Earhart and Edison and Coco Chanel and Annie Oakley. Even Nelson Mandela and Mother Teresa. All were masters of turning other peoples' will to their own, grander vision. All possessed the tenacity to press on, regardless of circumstance, and they never gave in, even under the most difficult circumstances.

Her theory is that the very best salespeople overcome adversity because they believe themselves to be fundamentally invincible.

They have the discipline to see constant challenge as a necessity for strength. Just as annealing steel makes it both strong and flexible. No matter what happens, they find a way to adapt, to negotiate, and to be successful, because there is no other viewpoint that matters. Is there really any better way to earn a living than in pursuit of achievement in business? Is there any human substitute for the pure empowerment of closing a deal? Isn't creating a deal the ultimate validation that the product you provide is fundamentally aligned with the progress of the marketplace?

. . . .

It's 4 AM and the stars trace a line of cool blue perforations in the flat sea just beyond the breakers. 135 degrees magnetic north brings the winter sun deep to her left along the beach with a slow rise hugging the horizon that, even at Christmas time, allows the high-vaulted windows of the Dreyfus beach house to collect the last of the late morning warmth into living area and onto the patio at the rear of the building. Jane squints at the horizon. She recalls her father's stories of the Nazi U-boat Wolfpacks hunting for Liberty ships in the coastal North Atlantic at night during the war. They were easy prey as they were silhouetted against the boardwalk in Atlantic City. Were it not for the impatient captain of a sister munitions ship, who had rushed ahead of his own ship into the path of two German torpedoes off the coast of Long Island on Christmas Eve 1943, Jane, her brother, and three sisters, and, in turn, their own children would not be alive today. It was a simple twist of fate that ended the chronicles of 38 lives, but enabled her own.

The great circle route of the ships supporting "Lend-Lease" relief guided them up into northern winter seas that were so cold and so dense that insurance carriers allowed a special "WNA," or Winter North Atlantic, Plimsol insurance mark on the bow, due to the added buoyancy. But when torpedoed in winter, at northern latitudes of 55° to 60°, the crewmen who escaped the killing blast faced the freezing brine that would slow-glaze bodies in their own adrenaline sweat before a rescue vessel could reach them.

The blue-gray light of dawn fills the air, and the cadence of the waves brings Jane slowly back to the physical present. Lifting her coffee to her lips, she steps right and strolls a few yards along the low stone perimeter facing the sea before turning right toward the turret-shaped addition that marks the southeast point of the house, and provides a lighthouse view of the horizon and Pistol Point Inlet to the south. She places the cup on the flattened head of carved Buddha by the entrance and ascends the spiral stairs to the exercise and meditation rooms on the second and third floors of the building. The walk leads past the Luini oil painting that she had copied while in Paris. She pauses, as always, to look into the di Vincian eyes of the woman's face, at once powerful, loving, and resolute in sacrifice. She pulls tightly on the belt of her white cotton Gi against the damp sea air now rising up the spiral stairs and out the opening between the French doors that accessed the high veranda crowning the tower-shaped stone addition. She lowers herself slowly to the floor, her spine assuming the familiar elongation. Her haunches are rooted to the mat and the oak floor, which is anchored in the stone wall founded in the concrete and ballast rock that is seated deeply in the sand and earth. She begins the breath that clears uncertainties, self-limiting self-talk, clears comparisons. She works to let go of wanting anything but the breath, and finally she let's go of wanting the breath. "I will stop when it no longer matters to stop." She is stealing a few minutes to re-charge her store of complete impartiality to whatever obstacle or achievement might come her way next. She is, was, will ever be prepared for it.

. . . .

"Jane Dreyfus, CEO of TradeRaider.com, Inc., State of California Bankruptcy Court, case number SM-4325." Jane's attorney, Ben Molinari, stands up and approaches the bench.

"Here, Your Honor."

"The court hereby confirms the plan for disposing of the Chapter 11 dissolution of the California corporation TradeRaider.com, Inc., and the assignment of the repayment of the outstanding debt to the CEO, Jane Dreyfus.

"Here are the documents, Your Honor."

"So ruled by the court. Are there any questions about the repayment agreement counselor?"

"Just one request, Your Honor. Ms. Dreyfus is planning to relocate to the state of Maryland. We wanted the court to be aware of this change from the information provided in the original petition, and advise the court that we will be providing notification of her new address and contact information as soon as the relocation is complete. In the mean time, any information regarding the bankruptcy filing can be communicated through my office."

Jane stares down at the heavy oak desk separating her from the judge's bench. It's facing edge is all sweat-stripped and stained from decades in the death grips of one financial capitulation after another. Jane reflects on the day that she and three ex-classmates from Berkeley agreed to create TradeRaider. After their meeting she stood before a mural at the Oakland airport, "Pioneers of Modern Aviation," which included an image of Amelia Earhart dashingly dressed in jaunty flight attire of her own design. She recalls the upwelling of excitement over the business plan that three old classmates from Berkeley had developed that would change — a web platform that would allow reverse auctioning of goods and services over the internet from any location on the globe. It would create a truly democratic marketplace for vendors looking to expand their market reach. The dream was to create a centralized, unbiased market for food goods where producers and cash buyers could transact directly — a "non-intermediated" market devoid of the payola and under-the-table dealing that plagued so many commodity markets.

At their first meeting, Jane had spoken passionately about the "buyer's school" tactics employed in the food business. What she observed among many legacy operators was a disturbing shift toward politically based decision-making in which the first principle was to "cover your ass," and the second was to make an ass out of the salesperson by leveraging their emotional commitment to extract as much "free consulting" as possible. The buyer was always a salaried employee of a business, so it seemed to Jane that their professional responsibility was to make critical decisions based on what was in the best interests of the employer. Not a bad thing in and of itself, just a fact of life. But the number of "corporate accrual payments" — little more than clever payola systems in one flavor or another — was growing to dominate vendor account management at both national and regional players. A few remarkable companies seemed to have developed immunity to what amounted to corporate kick-back systems, often on a grand scale. It was reminiscent of the turn-of-the-century scheming of the robber barons, like Vanderbilt and Gould, who regularly carried suitcases filled with cash to congressman and bureaucrats to secure coveted rail routes. In retail, it is coveted shelf space or slots, and in distribution it is SKUs in the warehouse. It was often not the payment for goods that made business happen. It was the payment for access that made deals happen.

She recalled a near-dawn meeting early in her career in the office of the buyer for U.S. Stores at the company's massive distribution facility near San Jose. Only after delivering her standard canned presentation about the history and competency of her company, followed by the financial strength, quality, customer service, blah, blah, blah, did she notice that on a bulletin board above and to the left of the buyer's head were five $100 bills neatly pinned next to a big yellow smiley face button.

By the end of that meeting she had agreed to a cash payment of one half of one percent on all paid invoices, to be delivered at a breakfast meeting the first Saturday of the quarter at a diner near Hollister. While, waiting in the parking lot for their third meeting, Jane noticed her customer pulling up in a brand-new oversized pick-up truck. He strangely and nervously blurted out, "A little gift from Win Tongbang . . .," as she met him climbing down the two steps to the truck's cab. He was equally uneasy as he announced to her that their deal was terminated. The 12-cylinder, 525-horsepower Dodge Ram pick-up had been delivered to his driveway in the middle of the night — keys left in the mail box with an unsigned note reading, "Whatever it takes." He joked with her about placing his family in the "witness protection program," and that he had become so paranoid that he suspected that they were being watched that very moment by someone who would report his movements back to Tongbang.

TradeRaider, Inc., provided a platform that, once and for all, eliminated the inefficiencies and corrupting forces of commoditized markets by providing a third-party, independent, and auditable information trail to ensure transparency in the buying and selling of food products directly between manufacturers and the end users. It would have a revolutionary impact on the industry, delivering transactions, fulfillment, and logistics all in one place at no additional cost to either the buyer or seller — the digital equivalent to the open outcry system in commodity futures markets. The business plan was solid, and the technology was robust, built and tested by a group of geniuses at Stanford for use in the financial markets.

Jane felt so timely and certain of success that she had chosen to preempt any market testing and go directly to Wall Street and Silicon Valley to peddle the plan to investment bankers such as Armand Whiterider; HMDB Capital; and Jenner, Lusk & Dare (JLD). That was the spring of 2001, and though money had tightened up, there was still keen interest in any innovative internet concept, especially on the heels of the book "B2B Exchange," which extolled the power of internet-based auctioning to revolutionize the future of business procurement operations.

. . . .

Antoine Pascal meets Jane outside the 42nd Street entrance to Grand Central Station. His statuesque frame and impeccable dress attests to his aristocratic upbringing, and his education at the prestigious INSEAD Paris. He had been introduced by a mutual friend, Ramos Costas, a Ph.D. candidate that Jane met when she was an undergrad. During a dinner at Tadich Grill, Jane and Costas discussed a business plan based on the new "B2B" platform internet technology. Costas had brought along a colleague he'd met at Stanford while studying for his MBA. PJ Louder is a brilliant software engineer who co-founded Cash-Clik, one of those rare gems that have come from the recent boom in internet-based businesses being mined in the Valley. When the Tadich conversation got around to funding, Crowder suggests Pascal as a candidate for matching the platform idea up with eager New York investors hungry to get in on the action.

Pascal works as the director of "technology verticals" at Whiterider, the investment banking firm in Manhattan. Whiterider is the proving ground for a number of the era's most brilliant traders and investment bankers, including the legendary Tom "Tex" Elliot. Coincidently, they had met before. Pascal had captured Jane's imagination during a chance introduction by her college roommate in a Palo Alto restaurant just six months prior. He waxed historical about how fortunes were being made in the Valley by young entrepreneurs sketching web-based "dinosaur killers" designed to terminate the inefficiencies of outmoded, commoditized businesses. Plans directed at "disintermediating" old models were being funded abundantly, based on the thinnest of value propositions, and the plans were securing abundant funding from an "exploding number" of "V.C.s"

Such firms and funds are desperate to be part of the Mother Lode of internet valuations, touted in weekly headlines of the new Technology Section of the Wall Street Journal. The opportunity to marry the B2B technology with the inefficiencies of the global food trade seems to have limitless growth potential, and Jane's conversation with Pascal escalated quickly to a call for a platform and a business plan.

Pascal had set up three appointments for their presentation that day: one with Frank Morello in Pascal's office at Armand Whiterider, one with Barry Einhorn at HMDB Capital, and the third with Duke Parnell, head of investment banking at JLD. With input from Pascal's colleagues at the firm, the business plan had been finely tuned, and they had rehearsed the presentation on video tape until the segues between them were flawless. The next morning they would complete the tour with a visit to Silicon Alley Investment Bank's Cam Snyder.

Jane is enthralled by the notion that TradeRaider is about to make business history. She daydreams about how this platform will change the face of global commerce in food products, connecting the maker and the marketer at a level of logistical efficiency heretofore never achieved. Prices will be more reflective of actual supply and demand. Producers will be guided by the digital market to greater quality and efficiency. Transportation and packaging costs will be optimized. And then there is the possibility to add a futures function that would allow buyers and sellers to hedge capacities forward, all with TradeRaider collecting a "house cut" on each transaction.

Now, staring down at the menu at the Water St. Deli, after a day hiking up and down Broad Street in Manhattan, in and out of the galleried offices of the rich and powerful, the entire plan seems a pitiful joke. There was never a chance that it could have secured funding. And, in retrospect, even if the concept was sound, the idea of presenting investment funds with a business plan (which, at that point, was little more than one fantasy on fine linen paper), seemed supremely short-sighted. The entire internet-funding environment had transmuted virtually overnight from from "HOT. com" to "NOT.com." The level of caution in the eyes and the words of the fund managers meeting with Jane and Pascal over the prior 36 hours verged on paranoia. Risk capital was becoming considerably more risky. Burn rates were exceeding the tolerance of the check writers to fund them, and it became apparent that, at least in Manhattan, the wheels had come off of what had been a two-year run of the internet B2B juggernaut. And it would soon become a worldwide phenomenon.

&

CHAPTER 2

"Jane, you are just too damn intense!"

Ryan Brickman is President of Seven Seas, a global seafood production and distribution company with operations in everything from the king crab fishery in Alaska to shrimp farms in Vietnam. His tall, thin frame barely fills his black Brooks Brothers suit, and, combined with his deep-set eyes and angular bearded face, gives him a more professorial Lincoln-like appearance than that of a hard-driving owner and leader of an international food conglomerate.

"You've done a terrific job of bringing in Newday, but we're turning the account over to Bob for a while."

Jane flashes back to her life at seven: It's midnight, she's sneaking out the back door of the little pink split-level, a peanut butter sandwich packed in the cardboard shoebox stubbornly snugged under her arm. She'd stolen her brother's pocket knife, three dollars, and two books of S&H Green Stamps, and crammed it all into the pockets of her red-plaid wool coat. After seeing the movie "Toby Tyler" at the Music Hall, she'd made up her mind that the very next time they punished her she would run way and join the circus. It didn't take long. After a screaming fit about who was, and who wasn't, allowed to enter her room, she was sent up without dinner. So she was going, at least as far as four PB&Js could get her on a cold February night.

She turns to the window, her hands planted on her hips. Stepping up to the glass with her head down, she pauses momentarily to compose herself before raising her eyes and staring out over the bay to the Marin headlands with unveiled indignation. Christ, she thinks, that "scary girl" thing again. What does she care? She has always overcome any obstacle she confronted. She doesn't even care to ask about the "intense" comment. She's heard it before. Intense, intimidating, passionate, pushy, even scary.

Carl Christian is vice president of procurement at Newday Foods, and Jane and he have never gotten along. To Jane he is the worst kind of buyer: confidently "greased" and glad to take free consulting from any sales exec with the stupidity to hand it over to him. It was well known around the industry that Christian is being paid off by Tongbang Brothers, the giant San Diego-based seafood company that has moved aggressively into the U.S. market following an explosion of imported seafood from China.

In the early 1980s, the growing trade imbalance was generating a surplus of U.S. dollars in China. Chinese manufacturers felt compelled to find ways repatriate their dollar earnings so they could purchase securities, real estate, and other fixed assets, effectively tax free. There was growing interest in finding "invisible" routes for the rivers of cash to circumvent the fixed exchange rates in China, and bypass the U.S. FinCEN reporting laws.[1]

Tongbang Brothers is a commodity shoe manufacturer, and the company faced the cash issue until they discovered the burgeoning Chinese shrimp trade. Shrimp was a high-liquidity, low-efficiency export market that was in rapid expansion between China and the U.S. Fueled by a coastal development initiative, artisanal farmers in the 1980s and '90s were grub-staked by the Chinese central government to expand the aquaculture industry along China's 7,500-kilometer rural coastline. With no organized commodity markets, the trade was a virtual monopoly. Harvested shrimp was purchased by feudal factory owners in Yuan, then processed cheaply in country, and sold at huge profits to the West as a luxury food product. Highly fragmented U.S. distribution markets provided the perfect environment for Shanghai-class corruption, and the Tongbang Brothers became the uncontested masters of the trade. With a fearless lack of restraint, they would launder as much as $10 million per month back into U.S. banks, with margins of 20-30 percent. The only problem was finding a highly liquid market to move the products. The unwitting and cash hungry retail sector was the ideal conduit. A number of the older U.S. grocery store chains, such as Newday, had been mismanaged for years, and by the 1980s was governed principally by the mission of selling its retail "real estate" to the highest bidder.

---

1   The mission of the U.S. Department of the Treasury Financial Crimes Enforcement Network (FinCEN) is to enhance U.S. national security, deter and detect criminal activity, and safeguard financial systems from abuse by promoting transparency in the U.S. and international financial systems. Among FinCEN's regulations is the requirement to report all physical movement of cash into or out of the U.S. that exceeds $10,000.

Carl Christian, like a number of key buyers in the country, succumbed to Tongbang Brothers' seductive combination of cash, sex, and intimidation. Win Tongbang is the mastermind responsible for building the family business through his keen instincts and a strategy of graft and extortion that he has refined to an art form. To suit his ambitions, he had cultivated a base "friends" at the highest levels of management in the retail grocery arena. Further, his powerful political connections enable him to maneuver around the U.S. Food & Drug Administration, the Department of Commerce, and the alphabet soup of U.S. federal and state agencies responsible for regulating food trade.

Tongbang Brothers "owns" Christian. None the less, Jane managed to build a solid base of business with the Newday company through a strategy of aggressively pursuing each of the Newday's regional buying offices, effectively cutting out corporate. The ebb and flow of centralized to decentralized purchasing was in her favor, and she's capitalized on it to Christian's distraction. In spite of Tongbang Brothers' command over Christian, his purchasing authority had begun to wither, mainly extending to setting strategic direction, but incapable to issuing actual purchase orders. Purchasing departments are often perceived as the evil, but necessary, stepchildren, and are kept at bay by periodically taking away their privileges. In the current cycle, the actual purchase orders were originating at the five regional operating offices. Jane has flanked Tongbang Brothers by taking advantage of this gap in the logistics, and she is marketing aggressively to the regional buyers. Christian is powerless to intercede directly in the Seven Seas business without drawing more attention to his own tenuous arrangement with Tongbang Brothers, and he resents it.

But Christian's irritation with Jane pales in comparison to Win Tongbang's contempt for Ryan Brickman, going far beyond his Taipan-class conceit about the "Seigweilo" — the white devils. As a U.S. manufacturer, Brickman has railed in the trade press against what he refers to as the "Asian contagion," and the incursion of Asian seafood producers who are dumping low-cost product into the U.S. market, undermining the domestic players and the jobs they provided. Though his xenophobia is purely strategic, it has successfully touched off a rally of industry outrage against the likes of Tongbang Brothers, leading to an antidumping investigation. The U.S. government's decision to penalize Tongbang Brothers and other importers for damaging the domestic industry with their flood of shipments is threatening enough to Tongbang's successful laundering formula. But it is Jane Dreyfus' relentless marketing to the Tongbang Brothers power base in retail grocery that frightens and enrages Win Tongbang. If Seven Seas can muster the U.S. government against him, what will prevent a polarization of the entire retail sector with its super sensitivity to public relations and public image? To hedge the liquidity that national retail chains provided, Tongbang tried to consolidate his grip on the business by hiring Caucasian sales staff, and directing them to call on divisional-level buyers. But Seven Seas has "first mover's advantage," and as the business gradually began slipping away, Tongbang has become increasingly desperate. He pounded Christian to get Seven Seas out of Newday, and, knowing that Jane spearheads their retail offensive, Christian called Brickman, insisting that she be taken off the account. Sensing Christian's desperation, Brickman angrily relented, agreeing to replace Jane on the account.

"Jane, I'm sending you to Brussels, to the food show."

Jane turns her attention from the window overlooking the docks to looking out over San Francisco Bay and the Marin headlands beyond.

"We're giving a presentation to some Icelandic bankers. They've heard about our brand's success in the club stores, and they want to get in on it. And I want them in. You're the one who put us there, so I want you to do a talk to them about Seven Seas and our growing retail business. Nothing too detailed, just your normal business expert stuff. Do your charts and numbers thing. Bankers love that. You'll charm the money out of them. You're good at that. I should know."

Jane rises from her chair, walks slowly toward Brickman, and leans against the desk.

"I'm sorry, Ryan, but I'm confused. What are you trying to tell me? Because I thought my job was making sales deals. I'm VP of Sales, right, not the CEO and not a partner. I've got the Hoffman deal running, which is on fire right now. It's June and we're just a couple of months out before we need to start delivering. That is, unless you are preparing to tell me about that stock deal you keep promising me."

Brickman rises to his feet and lowers his voice.

"Jane you're strung too tight. You're scaring people. Make this a mini-vacation. Take a few days off. You can catch the train to Paris and London. It's on the company. You deserve it. You don't have to stay for the whole show. Just do the presentation and take off. Enjoy yourself."

"I'd rather have the stock."

"You'll get the stock. Just tell me what you want. This is your business anyway. I can't run things forever, and I'm going to need to turn it over. You are the one. I mean, who else its there?"

"Ryan, I'm sorry, but you've said it before. Frankly there are lots of ways things could go if something happened to you. I just want to know where I'm going, that's all. If you can't answer that question, just tell me."

"Yes I can. You're with me. Get over to Brussels and relax. I promise I'll have something worked out soon. I'll put Mike on it. Deal?"

Jane's office is closer to the waterfront — a floor lower in the building, but just above the wharf itself. The trawlers come up to unload just 50 yards from the door below her desk, and there is something comforting about the gentle rocking of the building each time a big boat, heavy-loaded with salmon or crab sidles up and nudges the pier. The rumble of the big Cummins engines travels up through the pre-war pilings and into the floors and walls of her office. It is a good money sound.

Jane hated fish when she first arrived in San Francisco. It was the 1980s, and the only job she could get was as a union fish cutter. But the business had gotten into her blood, and the fresh-cut cucumber smell of iced salmon coming over the rail of the boat was imprinted in her DNA the way that anadromous fish imprint the mineral code of the headwaters of the rivers that spawned them. That imprint is so powerful that the fish return in massive "herds" year after year, generation after generation, stampeding back to their source.

Jane had worked in the Alaska fishery since her junior year in college, when she landed a job with NOAA, collecting economic data on pollack fisheries. "You know, it's the stuff they make imitation crab out of," she would tell her friends.

She had loved Alaska from her very first view of the "magnificent desolation." She returned after her undergraduate years at Berkeley to work for the U.S. Department of Commerce as a monitor of foreign fishing operations in the so-called Bering Sea "donut hole," a rich, 90,000-square-mile fishery lying beyond the 200-mile limit of territorial waters that are managed by either the U.S. or Russian governments. The perimeters of control resulted in a circular zone in the center of the Bering Sea that is virtually unprotected. It is a "Wild West" free-for-all for foreign fishing operations that, having tapped out their local fisheries, seek to exploit the relatively bountiful and unrestricted fishing available in the "hole."

Her love of the business is reinforced by a genuine admiration for the fishermen, who daily wrest a living from deep and dangerous waters. A strong back, an affinity for exhaustive hours, and a tolerance for, or ignorance of, the deadly risks of high-seas fishing were required skills for the job. Others need not apply.

Recruiting her out of Alaska, Brickman had taught her about taking business risks, hedging the downside, and paying attention to the details. He taught her that the failure to communicate trouble immediately was as dangerous in business as it was at sea, and that it included any issue that could compromise the Seven

Seas brand and its reputation. But Brickman's most memorable lesson was about how business is conducted at the highest levels. At the top, where nothing is ever left to chance.

Brickman was hosting a dinner of company executives at the offices — a tradition at the close of each salmon season.

"Come with me. I'd like to show you something." His voice rumbles down from the right as she stood admiring the aerial photographs of the 13 Seven Seas factories that lined the coast from Eureka to Dutch Harbor.

Jane follows him down the corridor that leads from the conference room to his private office. He punches a pass code into the security key pad, and when the green light flashes, he opens the door. He walks over to the heavy door marked "Private."

"Have a seat, I'll just be a moment."

He unlocks the door, which Jane had always assumed to be a closet, and comes out carrying a large, black Samsonite suitcase. He hefts the suitcase onto the corner of his dark oak desk and pulls the keys from his pocket, fiddling for the small key that unlocks the hasp to the case.

"My God, Ryan, what's this?"

As he opens it, she can see that the case is filled with neatly wrapped bundles of $50 and $100 bills. She looks stunned, and Ryan tries to balance her nerves with a little humor. "You need to air this stuff out once and a while or it will turn stale on you!"

He stifles a laugh with his tongue between his teeth, but can't suppress his pleasure at the scene. "I've got another one in there just like it. Over a million bucks. I really don't know exactly how much is there."

Sitting down at his desk, he removes a several stacks of $50s and $100s and begin counting. Jane sits transfixed by the suitcase full of cash. Oh, how this much money could transform my life, she thinks. No more struggling with the bills every month. No more monthly payments on her student loan. No more worries about paying off credit cards, and trying to figure out how she might squirrel away some money for savings.

"There," he says, matter-of-factly, "that's $9,900. You can never be too careful with cash. Count it every time you receive it. Even I make mistakes counting it, so before you hand it over be sure you count it first."

Brickman pulls several rubber bands and a large manila envelope with a string cinch from his desk drawer.

"I want you to take the shuttle to LA tomorrow, rent a car, and go to San Pedro. There's a restaurant there called Nero's. You know Bill Broward, the VP from Fortune Stores? He'll meet you at that restaurant.

Give him this envelope. He won't stay to eat, and he isn't big on small talk. After he leaves, wait 15 minutes, then head back to the airport. And by the way, don't use the pay phone outside of Nero's. It's tapped."

"Ryan, I've never handled this kind of thing for you. It's always Bob who does this stuff."

"I know, but he can't make it tomorrow and it needs to be taken care of. You'll do fine. Don't sweat it."

That night, driving home with the envelope is unnerving. What if something goes wrong? But nothing will go wrong. This is the way big business is done at high levels. Someone gets paid twice for violating their responsibility to both their company and their customer. Is this the way all business operates? Something for nothing in exchange for negligence? Is every Bill Broward in every position of purchasing authority being paid off in one way or another? There's a reason that they call it "grease," Jane reasons, and now she is part of it — a "mule" delivering cash to some two-bit grocery buyer. But this is also the system that is bringing Seven Seas massive profits and success.

Brickman once told her, after a trio of CC and rocks, "I was Snow White, but I drifted." He had explained how his customers in New York City had taught him the intricacies of accounting for payola. "It's all about the cash. Once we learned to create and manage volumes of it, the sky was the limit. Cash buys more cash. It is a law of nature."

Though Jane's business is, so far, untainted by payoffs, she has been approached from time to time and has, so far, walked away. But the really big deals have eluded her, and though she always suspected it, the truth is now beginning to sink in. The primary outcome Broward is looking for isn't the performance of his company or even his department. It is accumulating as much cash as he can, with the least possible risk. And Ryan Brickman is providing the least-risk path for achieving that outcome.

More than being just a "bag man," Brickman's assignment for Jane is a test. The next morning, she recalls his words. She recounts the money before her flight, and discovers there is an extra $100 bill in one of the stacks. She counts it again. Still $10,000. She removes one of the $100 bills, re-bands the stack, and returns the bundle to the envelope. The rest goes flawlessly, except, because she is so nervous, when she gets to the airport she inadvertently walks into the men's room, much to the surprise of the guy she runs into after she notices the urinals.

She arrives at Nero's early and sits nervously in the booth while gazing out the rear picture window of the restaurant. The view is of the San Pedro Channel, but the entire frame is filled by a cruise ship slowly gliding by. It is so monstrously close that it dwarfs the surroundings as if by some uncanny power that travels with it, transforming human scale to miniature then back again.

"Jane Dreyfus?" The heavy "whiskey 'n' tabacca" voice croaks out unexpectedly into the background of clinking china. She is startled, but regains her composure.

"Hello Bill." She reaches up to shake hands, but he has already turned away from her and toward the front counter, motioning to the waitress for coffee. He reaches out his right hand, grasping the back of the opposite seat, leaning over it as if searching for something he is missing. It is then that Jane sees the gun. A black holster is tucked into the hollow just alongside his right rib cage. She can't take her eyes off of it. His eyes carefully scan the seat across from her, and seeing it empty, he proceeds to sit down, repeating the same surveillance of the table top.

After clearing his throat and eyeing the table top and the surroundings, he turns to Jane.

"Listen Jane, I don't have a lot of time, so if we can get moving here I'd appreciate it."

It suddenly occurs to Jane that her instructions were to put the envelope on the seat when she saw Broward arrive. He would pick it up, order coffee, wait a few minutes, and leave.

She grabs her purse and, after fidgeting with the hasp for what seems an interminable time but is actually about ten seconds, she produces the brown envelope that Brickman had given her. Smiling gleefully at the prospect of finally delivering the cash, she hands the thinly disguised rubber-banded envelope across the table to Broward for all within public eyeshot to see, as clearly as if it had been captured on an FBI surveillance video. His astonishment at her indiscretion is palpable, and, on retrieving the package, his face flushes red, and his eyes dart about the room looking for anyone who might have seen it happen. With little ado, he rises and heads for the door. As he exits the restaurant Jane is too nervous to eat and asks for the check. She then heads for LAX and the 45-minute flight back to San Francisco.

The next morning she climbs the stairs to Brickman's office and gently knocks on the closed door.

"What is it, Arnold? I'm on the phone!"

"Sorry, Ryan, it's Jane, I'll come back."

"No wait, I'll be just a minute."

As she waits, she fidgets with the extra $100 bill, rolling it and folding over and over. I could use this hundred right now, she thinks. He'll never notice the mistake. Christ, there's a million in cash in there. He even told me that he didn't know exactly how much he had. He admitted that he made mistakes himself when counting cash.

"Hey Jane, get in here."

As she enters the room Brickman is seated at his desk, peering down at inventory numbers through black, half-rimmed reading glasses. His trademark Don Diego Lonsdale cigar juts from the corner of his mouth. He lifts his head and removes his glasses as a Cheshire-cat smile creeps across his face.

"So Killer, how did it go?"

Unable to contain the struggle any longer she blurts out a confession. "There was an extra hundred in the stack. I recounted it before I left for the airport and it counted an extra hundred. Here," she says, holding out the bill.

"Bring it over here."

Ryan reaches across the desk, and takes the bill from her hand. He opens the top drawer and removes a plain, white, legal-sized envelope, opens it, and puts the bill inside. He tucks the flap of the envelope inside and hands it to Jane.

"Here's a thousand for you. This was a test. If you hadn't returned the $100 I would have fired you. Because you did, I'm giving you a raise, effective immediately."

. . . .

Sales has taught Jane that there are two types of people in the business world — and they are not the obvious buyers and sellers. Instead, they're the makers and the takers.

The makers are creators. They seek out opportunities to create new business, new revenues, and new enterprise. Typically these are the sellers, the entrepreneurs, the self-determinists. They take the chances. They try new things. They're open to new ideas. They risk their money and their futures on a roll of the dice of commerce, and they live with the consequences, always confident that, regardless of the outcome, they can — and will — rise above it to try again. They have an indomitable spirit and a bloodhound's nose for good numbers that is programmed into their DNA. And when they fall down they get back up and try again.

Then there are the takers. The hoarders and the "hand-outers." The cheaters, liars, and misanthropes. Those who see dark clouds surrounding every silver lining. The cynics. Those who acquire authority and revert to milking it instead of making something out of it. The self-contented, those are the takers.

Jane hates the takers, and she has learned to pick them out in a heartbeat. She can tell them by their one-sided, buttoned-down attitude, their self-consumed demeanor and persistent lack of creativity and intelligence. What she most loves about sales is that, in its purest form, it is about getting paid for creating opportunities. It's about discovering the path to new and exciting outcomes in business — going beyond the transactional mechanics to making new things happen, making deals happen.

Jane had taken Brickman a bold and innovative merchandising plan, radically different from anything his competitors could match. It included detailed tactical strategy for channeling more of the big-spending seafood shoppers into the highly profitable section of the store perimeter.

The few truly collaborative customers she deals with are of what kept her sane in the business. They are generally smaller firms where Jane is able to deal directly with the senior management on a regular basis. These are great relationships, she knows, but still, there is something missing in her approach. The customers come and go too fast. The challenge always is to keep the business vital and growing. To keep the business relationships engaging and innovating. What is lacking in her approach? She has always built her business on dogged pursuit of a client. A true hunter's mentality. She is known for beating prospects into submission with her tenacity. Prospects, clients, and colleagues occasionally mention her overbearing style. But she always writes it off as a good thing. After all, isn't a dominant personality, a driven, no-nonsense approach a positive thing in business?

Look at Ryan Brickman, her role model. Isn't he the personification of the dissatisfied entrepreneur: always pushing, always striving to create more? As she sees it, this attitude is characteristic of the American spirit. The "Way of the West." She likes it. The idea is no nonsense and straight talk. "What do we need to get it done?" is her mantra. Her heroes live that ethic in one manner or another. Now she is being told by her own mentor that she should ease off. It just doesn't make sense. If the customers can't deal with her forthright personality well, let's find customers that can. She values the freedom of speaking her mind and running her own show. Of being in control. It's intoxicating. Now she faces the question of what's she willing to give up to preserve that freedom, which she cherishes so highly. The answer comes back to her forcefully: Nothing at all. Conducting her life, first and foremost, in accordance with the rules and principles established by herself and for herself is all that really matters, and those rules and principles should never be violated. Everything else is secondary.

ॐ

CHAPTER 3

Preparing to board the 777 for Brussels, Jane's mind is filled with a flood of untied loose ends. She is on her cell with Doug Minello, her assistant. Doug was recommended to Brickman through their banker, and Brickman had insisted that she interview him to handle sales detailing as her number two, because details are not her strength. He is an ex-Franciscan priest who fell in love with a nun he met when they worked together on an inner-city project for unwed mothers. In time, their love surpassed their devotion to their vows, and they left the church and married. Doug was responsible for organizing outreach projects for the archdiocese, and in the course of that work had become a master at both planning and persuading. During their three years of working together, Jane has come to depend on Doug to handle the day-to-day details of her sales activities — everything from issuing marketing agreements, to customer service and bird-dogging potential disasters, to booking her travel arrangements. It was Doug who had put her on Virgin's San Francisco-to-Heathrow flight so she could stop and deal with a problem in closing the deal with Hoffman-UK before taking the Eurostar to Brussels for the show. From there it would be the train to Paris to meet Bunge, then back to London for the ride home.

She depends on Doug to handle sales details such as collecting signed agreements, but Hoffman had begun spinning out of control.

She is struggling with how to nail down a commitment from the UK portion of the corporate contract. It is becoming a serious compliance problem, and Jane knows that compliance by divisions on corporate deals rests squarely on the back of the vendor in the food industry, and that trouble with one division could easily spread to the whole organization. With clear program instructions from the "Mother Ship" U.S. corporate office, she had expected that Nigel Howard and his UK crew would just fall into line. But Howard has ignored her e-mails, and dodged her calls. After six weeks with no progress, and the 60-day merchandising deadline approaching, she decided to bring in a local "hired gun" to make it happen. Winning Hoffman has never been easy, and as she slides into her seat and peers out over the tarmac to the brooding weather she recalls the first time she met face-to-face with the CEO Herb Hoffman.

Eleven months earlier, Jane stood on the porch outside the lobby of Hoffman's main building, which was positioned in the center of an immaculate office complex on the outskirts of Portland. The setting was the antithesis of the typical grocery retailer's corporate offices. It was open and spacious — a design with lots of glass and vaulted ceilings. From across the small lake that hugged the perimeter of the campus drifted the pungent aroma of redwood and good management. And both towered over the buildings that lined the serpentine drive to the main lobby. This was a tranquil setting that belied the intense energy of the celebration going on inside. Jane could hear the chanting and outcries from

the auditorium, which was annexed to the lobby, where Herb
Hoffman was holding one of his ritual convocations for staff
and management. He did this each time a new store reached its
first net profit number: the volume of business necessary for the
store to cover its operational costs at the fixed 18.5 percent gross
product margin.

Hoffman is as legendary for his showmanship as he is for his
intense focus on every detail of operations, and his relentless waves
of intercompany communications, which often are cc'd to every
manager in the organization. He dismisses the Wall Street critics
who chide him for paying the highest wages and having, by far,
the best employee benefit package of any of his competitors. Some
early rank-and-file employees have become wealthy because of
Hoffman's aggressive employee stock-option program. Turnover
was only a fraction of their competitors' in the historically
high-attrition retail industry, and Herb Hoffman was damn proud
of it.

Jane's appointment was with the Hoffman team responsible for
frozen foods, and she was nervous. Her pitch was typically (for
her) confrontational, which was not a problem. But the stakes were
high this time. Hoffman was a huge account, and her competitors
were the largest food companies in the world. But she was well
prepared for the attack, and had pumped herself up to be ready
for anything.

She had learned during an Asian sourcing trip that Hoffman's
current supplier was using chemical additives in their food
products to increase the water-weight and, thereby, decrease their
costs. This was a common practice in the industry, but because

the FDA did not enforce additives laws when it came to seafood, many companies viewed the laxity as a free ticket to create profits by adding as much water as possible during processing. Water was free, and with shrimp, for example, selling at $5-10 per pound, the opportunity for abuse was irresistible. But Hoffman had strict internal guidelines regarding the foods they sold, requiring each manufacturer to fully disclose the contents on the label. Tongbang Brothers was violating the rule, and publicly denying that their product contained anything but pure, all-natural shrimp. Armed with the evidence, she was determined to use it to win the account for Seven Seas. She had written a business plan to elevate the quality of the entire seafood program, and that plan would make Hoffman the only national seller of non-chemically-treated seafood products.

"Jane?" It was Paul Stinball's voice, and she turned to see him leaning out the door to the lobby.

"Another beautiful day in the City of Roses, right?" Jane stretches out her hand and smiling. "You're always complaining about the rain up here, but every time I visit the sun is shining. Not a cloud in the sky."

"Jane, I hope you have your facts right, because Win from Tongbang Brothers has been on the phone with Herb. After all, shrimp is big business for us, and he has all of it."

Jane took a deep gulp. "Paul, my source is rock solid, and I brought the phosphate tests performed in Vietnam, on samples taken in your own stores. Fact is, your shrimp is heavily pumped."

They proceeded to the elevator and up to the second floor. Cindy Clancy and Tom Griffin greeted Jane as she entered the conference room — a Spartan internal space devoid of windows, and with a long white board and projection screen. A video-conferencing device sat in the center of the table. Otherwise, the walls were adorned with one framed piece of art — a painting of a grizzly bear grasping a giant Sockeye salmon as it leapt up a river rapids. Below the painting was the Mission Statement, touting how the Hoffman company always strives to provide better products at a lower overall cost.

Neither Tom nor Cindy got up as she entered the room. The questioning began defensively at first, and Jane sensed that the team was determined to debunk her findings. She decided not to fight it. She allowed them all to unload on her before presenting the facts. About ten minutes into the conversation the door swung open and Herb Hoffman entered the room. Jane stood up to greet him, but he waved her down.

"Jane, what's the big idea coming here and telling us that we are selling our 12 million customers tainted shrimp? I've never even heard of your company before, and Hoffman has been doing business with our current supplier for more than 15 years. I know him personally."

"Well, Mr. Hoffman . . ."

"Don't give me that 'Mister' crap. Doesn't work on me. It's Herb." Jane blanched at the idea that Hoffman had interpreted her formality as a tactic to get her to suck up to him.

"Herb, of course I want your business. And I know that what I am about to tell you doesn't guarantee me anything. But, frankly, I'm hoping it opens the door, that's all."

Jane cast her eyes around the table for some sign of confirmation but instead was greeted with roaring apathy at the mere suggestion. Buyers responsible for seven-figure purchasing were remarkably cold-blooded. Over the years, Herb Hoffman had brought in a number of negotiating trainers, like Karas and Anderson, to provide intensive training in formal negotiations. They went deep into the art and psychology, and the strategies and tactics, of dealing with vendors. Hoffman, in particular, was known for thorough preliminary evaluation and advanced training of their buying staff. Their behavior was adapted to remain dispassionate in the purchasing process, staying focused exclusively on creating outcomes that were best fit for Hoffman's strategic plan – not for the vendor's plan. All employees of the company, even down to the warehousemen, submitted to psychographic evaluations to ascertain their attitude, trainability, and ethical disposition for decision-making. A zealot's belief in doing always and everywhere what was best for Hoffman's was required. Either you were in all the way, or you were out.

"Herb, I appreciate what this news means to your people, and the implications for your other vendors. I'm telling you flat-out that the product you are putting in your stores as 'all natural' is loaded with chemical hydrators and preservatives. Here's the report I referred to, conducted by Sullivan Labs using samples taken here in the U.S. and in Camau from cartons and bags with your name on them. But the real reason I'm here isn't to torpedo one of my competitors. It's to talk with you about a new program I'm proposing that will deliver a far superior product. It's a signature program that will be exclusive and unique to Hoffman, and an important value to your customers who want to buy honest, natural food products. What I don't know . . .", she cast her eyes around the table and then back to Hoffman, ". . . is this important to you?"

The Outcome

CHAPTER 4

While stepping through the hatchway into the 777, Jane reaches out ritually to anoint the fuselage, like the priest with chrism had done when her Catholic grandmother took her to a Mass as a child. "Thou art dust, and dust thy shall return," he intoned.

She busies herself with the Hoffman presentation on the flight across to pick up east coast passengers before continuing on to Heathrow. Rising over Newark, the patterns in the lights below slowly reveal themselves with the increasing altitude. The lights of the BP refinery next to the airport quickly cluster and disappear as the big jet carves a hard left, rising up along the shaft of Manhattan and crossing the lights marking the approach to the George Washington Bridge and Cross-Bronx Expressway. Off the port side are the lights of the NE Thruway and the terrestrial nebulae marking the cities and towns straddling Interstate 95 as traffic is coursing its way to Boston and above. Jane's eyes are glued to the window. Even after a million miles, she still harbors a child-like fascination with being in the air. She had taken ground school once, and had begun flying herself. She had even bought a share in a Piper Arrow, but she had struggled with the cost. It's always the same aspiration that fills her mind looking down over any one of the 97 cities in 23 countries she has visited in the course of her career.

She leans her seat back, closes her eyes, and lets it all go into the press of the engines at her back powering the plane aloft. She thinks about the extraordinary creative power of the human imagination to explore and to build. What will be her contribution to this web of civilization that stretches out over the planet? Will she bring to the millions of businesses that, in concert, form the cardiac pulse of mankind's adventure on this tiny ball in space. Long ago she had realized that with all of its flaws, business represents the best aspirations of mankind — the great vector of human progress. She is the kind of citizen who's driven by the will to create value and usefulness, and has the discipline and courage to place their creations into the market for the world to buy or not. That's the determinant aspiration of every important civilization and the aggregate of its members. Commercial enterprise, painter, prospector, capitalist, or communist — it always comes back to the essential notion of bigger, better, faster. The cognoscenti of this simple law are the makers: The ones who move mankind forward. And to Jane, salespeople are the change-agents of those great civilizations. They drive out the old and bring in the new. At their finest, they are both the deliverer and enabler of human innovation. They build the bridges between what is now and what will be.

The plane banks a few degrees right, followed immediately by a big bounce, as it slices upward through some cirrus clouds and begins leveling off.

"Pardon me, but I just spilled some of my drink and I think . . ."

For the first time since boarding Jane looks to her right at her seat mate. He has a thin aristocratic face with a shock of blond hair, greying near the temples. He is dressed in an exercise outfit — most appropriate for the six-hour overnight flight, but fashionably awkward with the black socks and the blue rally-striped pants and jacket and the sweatshirt that reads "UCSD Banana Slugs." He hands Jane a cocktail napkin with which she quickly soaks up the scotch that has splashed on the crimson fabric of the seat.

"David Shepard," he says, extending his hand over the arm rest with a slight smile. "I'm sorry for the mess. Actually, since it's a long flight I thought it might be a good way to break the ice."

Jane smiles weakly, casting her eyes down at the half-full glass of scotch, and waiting for the next set of bumps.

"Jane Dreyfus. And fair warning: there's usually more than one bump between here and London, so you'd better learn to hold on to that glass."

Jane usually loathes conversations with airplane seat mates. Experience has taught her that odds are the conversations on airplanes often become one-sided, with someone rambling on and on about how successful they are, or how much they travel, or how much they hate airline service. It isn't that Jane doesn't like talking. She just hates all the BS. She's had only had a handful of meaningful conversations on planes over the course of her travels. One was on Southwest to Albuquerque with a salesperson for Caterpillar. Another was with an Air Force pilot returning from Kandahar. And the third was on a first-class upgrade from Tokyo to San Francisco, when she happened to be seated next to a Nobel laureate whose lecture series Jane had attended at Cal-Berkeley.

Not foiled by Jane's stiff reply, Shepard continues, "Frankly, I'm often disappointed with airborne conversations. People usually go on and on about themselves, and then there's always that inevitable awkward moment when I'm ready to start in on a book that I've looked forward to reading for weeks, or just want to take a nap, and I end up struggling for a way you break off the conversation. You know what I mean?"

Jane nods at the coincidence that he had spoken to exactly what was going through her mind, and raises her eyebrow with a slight smile in acknowledgment of the point.

"Again," he continues, "this is a long flight, so what do you say we set an expectation right now. If either one of us wants to break off the conversation, we'll just hold up a hand, like in the dentist's office when he tells you to hold up your hand if there's any pain."

Jane barely stifles a laugh. "Well, if you expect that talking with you will be anything like a trip to the dentist, and then let me hold up my hand right now and get it over with." They both chuckle at her comment as the first officer cuts in overhead to announce that the plane has reached cruising altitude and that cabin service will begin shortly. The flight attendant, dressed smartly in Virgin red, takes their drink orders and follows by rolling up with a cart of hors d'oeuvres.

"I must say that your 'expectation setting' comment is an unusual way to begin a conversation."

Shepard cocks his head to the left, beaming a wise smile in her direction, as if he's heard the comment before.

"People loathe uncertainty." He clears his throat as if preparing to say something important. "Conversations are my specialty, and one principle of good conversation is to find a way to set expectations from right up front."

Jane turns her head slightly to the left and glances out at the night enveloping the plane, sipping slowly on her vodka-on-the-rocks. "I don't quite understand. Are you telling me that I should ask a person to hold up their hand like a dental patient."

"No, it's deeper than that. When you go to the dentist, he doesn't just grab the drill and start grinding away, right? He prepares you for what's coming. If he's giving you Novocain, he'll tell you: 'First you're going to feel a pinch, then it should begin feeling numb around the tooth.' If there's any pain what do they tell you to do?"

Before she answers he continues. "Before I enter into a business conversation with a prospect, they get the disclaimer: If, at any point in the conversation, either of us feels uncomfortable with the progress, and there's no 'fit,' let's agree that we just hold up our hand and conversation is over."

"Well, most of my conversations begin over the phone," Jane counters, "so we don't get the chance to raise hands." She looks him dead in the eye with this statement, seeking a rebuttal, because something about the "uncertainty" comment rang true for her, but she can't figure it out just yet.

"No, no, you're missing the point," he says. "It's not really about holding up your hand. It's about lowering the tension about the unknown. It's about the uncertainty. It's about making the point early on that you are not going to club them over the head. It's about showing deference so that the rest of your conversation can proceed toward a deeper and more candid level. After all, who wants superfluous small talk these days, especially in business? I mean, unless I know for certain that we share a passion for the Yankees, does it really make sense for me to start reciting the box score of yesterday's game. If I make a wrong guess, my credibility will suffer because assumptions are always wrong, even when the assumption itself turns out to be correct. Because we don't know each other, you'll find this off-putting and my credibility with you will suffer."

"I'm a Giants fan by the way, but I get your point. Expectation-setting is what you do to make the other person feel more comfortable, right? Sort of like common courtesy? But how does it work in business? I'm constantly in situations where I am meeting new people who I'd like to do business with, or who I'd like to have an open conversation with. Are you asking me to begin every one of those conversations by saying 'OK, before we get started we need to get a few ground rules straight.'? Now that seems awkward."

Shepard continues, "Business is about getting to the truth of a situation as quickly and efficiently as possible so that you can make decisions and move on. To that extent, business conversations are much different than personal conversations, which are more nuanced and less direct. What most sales people don't realize is that they are getting paid to create a least-risk path to the client's outcome. Whoever does it best, and first, will get the business. So the question becomes: How do we get the job done? How do we rise to the level of a true professional by being superb at getting the job done? It begins with expectation-setting. Prospects love the disciple of a salesperson who knows where she is going in the conversation, and has the self-confidence to take them there."

"It's David, right? David, what makes you think I'm in sales. Or even interested in sales?"

"That's easy. You're wearing a Rolex, which suggests that you're a 'Type D' personality. You either have money and always buy the best, or you don't, and are just trying to impress people. I suspect the latter, because the new shirt and jeans you're wearing are off a Macy's rack, not Nordstrom or custom tailored. Salespeople often try to project to people that they're successful with clothes and jewelry, when they really can't afford them. It's a mistake because, frankly, it has the opposite effect on the prospect. Second, your Day-Timer in the seatback pocket is brand new, which tells me that you don't have a secretary, so you're probably not in the C-Suite. You either just started a new time-management program, or you bought it because you rely on a customer relationship management system. You hate dragging your laptop around when you travel, but you don't want to rely on your Blackberry alone. Either way, these indicators tell me 'salesperson.'"

"I don't know whether to be astounded, or insulted, or both." Jane shakes her head as if she's trying to clear her thoughts. "Is this some special gift you have, or did someone teach you how to do it?"

"It's a little bit of both, actually." Shepard raises his glass in his right hand and extends his index finger upwards. "But to be honest with you, it helped to read the tag on your briefcase in the overhead before I sat down. 'Jane Dreyfuss, Vice President Sales, Seven Seas.' That's you, right?"

Jane turns to the window to rest her brain momentarily. From her forward seat, she can just see the red flashing navigation light on the port winglet. Stars fill her field of view, and she thinks about how flying the great circle eastward accelerates time, like fast forward with the plane and the sun racing together, at twice the speed of sound leading to a sudden sunrise somewhere over Iceland.

She has always carried a deeply buried indignity about being a salesperson. No parents ever stand over the crib, beaming with pride and expectation, and think, "I wonder if she'll grow up to be a doctor? A lawyer? Or just maybe, if we're lucky, a salesperson?" Much less a salesperson in the food business. Sure, everybody needs to eat, but only the Japanese need to eat fish. In Japan, selling seafood is an honorable profession. Daichi Umi, Japan's largest fish company, has the most prominent commercial building on the perimeter of the Imperial Palace compound. It is the only building with a line of sight that allows a view over the walls of the inner residence. They recruit the best business students, and pay the highest salaries. Here, selling is something different. She remembers Brickman telling her, when she had first approached him about a sales job, "There aren't many Rhodes Scholars in the seafood business. If you've got brains, you can make a lot of money here."

But it's interesting, she thinks, how the definition of ". . . a lot of money" changes as one matures. She has struggled lately with how to make important, "life-changing" money, and how she will need to raise her game to make it so.

She turns back from the window, preceding her response with a skeptical "Hmmm," and addresses Shepard. "Let me ask you a question about this expectation-setting concept of yours. Listen, you don't know the kind of prospects and clients I deal with. These people are cold-blooded killers. They're not looking for any candid conversation. They want the facts, and they want the payoff and price. That's it. 'What's in it for me' is everything to them. Do you know that the majority of the U.S. food retailing and distribution companies would be out of business if it weren't for sheltered income and accruals from manufacturers?"

As the flight attendant passes by, Shepard holds up his right hand and flashes the "V" sign. "Two more please."

"Look, Jane, your prospects are human beings, aren't they?"

"Sometimes I'm not so sure." Rolling her eyes, her brain begins to scan a rogue's gallery of her most recalcitrant customers and prospects. George Cameron immediately comes to mind. He is the most insipid and intractable of all of the buyers she has encountered, prone to promise one thing and blatantly do another. But the potential business from him is so large that Jane has kept him in the funnel, and continues spending countless hours trying to convert the account. She has spent sleepless nights staring at the ceiling each time a piece of promised business has fallen through at the eleventh hour, leaving her to making excuses to management on why it had all come apart, and feeling guilty about the money she burned in her efforts to nail down the account. Thanks to Cameron, she has finally become so self-conscious about the return on investment of her expenses that she's stopped sending in dinner receipts for any account wasn't a paying customer.

"David, I'll be honest with you. I don't know what to expect from my clients. There's no certainty at all in our business relationships. This business is different. In fact, it's impossible. One day everything is going as smooth as silk. The customers love us. Then the next day they're asking me for stock levels and giving me a termination date. The last thing I think about is my 'relationship' with these people. To them, it's all about the bottom line. 'What's in it for me?' That's the only expectation worth setting. Nothing else matters."

"Jane, I've been working with sales organizations for a long time, and they all think their sales issues are unique. But here's a CNN Update: The earth down there is round. What you describe is happening every day in millions of sales organizations across the planet. In fact, more so now than ever before, with the competitiveness of the global, digital marketplace. You're right. 'WIIFM' is everyone's favorite radio station, but not in the cynical sense that you are describing it. You need to define it at a higher level. Not necessarily good or bad, just what it is. To be a world-class sales person, it is mission-critical to excel at the vital human skills of creating business relationships, establishing what is expected from those relationships, then controlling the conversations to focus on achieving productive business outcomes from those relationships. That outcome is the reality of 'WIIFM.'"

CHAPTER 5

"David, can you hear me? OK, I get the 'expectation management' part. But you kept mentioning the relationship thing when we were on the plane. I don't buy it. I've done plenty to build relationships with my customers, and they still bail on me."

"Jane, I've just arrived at Bern-Belp. Can I call you back from the hotel?"

The Bellevue Palace Hotel is a classic luxury Grande Dame, adjacent to the towering bridge over the Aare River on Bern's Kochergasse. Shepard is the keynote speaker at a medical conference organized by one of his clients.

Shepard continues, "OK, I understand. Just think about this, Jane, 'til I can call you back. Relationship-building is not about making friends. It's about being relevant. Customers need funds, not friends. Got it? I'll call you back in about an hour."

Jane punches the "end call" button on her Blackberry and lies back on the pillow. She distracts herself until she can't be bothered otherwise by doing the mental arithmetic of what this trip is costing her and subtracting it from the $3,100 balance available on her Visa card. Since the bankruptcy, every trip she takes is a crash course in cash management. As a rule, her company does not provide credit cards, thus requiring employees to pay their own travel costs, then submit an expenses report for reimbursement. Ryan Brickman always uses the excuse that if he gave her a company card he would have to give everybody a card. So instead, she pays cash when she can, and uses her sole credit card (she previously had six) as cautiously as possible.

While launching the TradeRaider business it had never occurred to her that the downside of failing to find investors would be so devastating to her, financially and personally. Her presumption had always been that the seed capital would be used to cover the expenses that they had accumulated in setting up the business. The hardware, the software, and the attorney's fees alone had absorbed nearly all of the $50,000 in Jane's 401k (not including the penalties), plus another $25,000 of Antoine Pascal's money. Once the personal credit was maxed out, the business had unraveled. HP Credit was ringing her cell phone daily for payment updates until Jane finally relented and hired a moving and shipping service to retrieve the boxes from the co-location facility in Mountain View and return them to the company. When the dust had finally settled, she justified the whole disastrous affair to herself by acknowledging that it had cost her less than a Harvard MBA, and had probably left her with twice the practical business knowledge than she could ever accrue in a classroom. And all in just 18 months! Even three years later, she had be negotiating with a prospect over some eleventh-hour demand on a deal she thought was closed, when a bright red stop light went on in her head. She had agreed to concession after concession while pitching investors on TradeRaider, and not a single one of 11 firms she had approached came through with the cash in the end.

Lesson learned? In business, never promise to give away something without getting something back in return.

"David?"

"Who the hell's David?"

"Ryan, sorry. I was expecting a call from someone I met on the plane." There's an audible chuckle on the other end of the phone.

"Really. Sounds interesting. But another time. We had a call from Gus Jambon, and he's a little nervous about the specification change on the Hoffman orders."

"Ryan, I told you both not to worry about it. This is clearly a higher quality than they are getting from their other suppliers. And the special cut is just added value. They'll be thrilled, and we'll look like heroes. By this time next year you'll have all of the divisions, and you and Sarah will be vacationing in the south of France."

"I know, I know. Do me a favor, Killer. Just give Gus a call and settle him down."

"OK, I will. But do me a favor. Pick up a book called 'Just Stop Guessing,' by David Shepard. You're going to be glad I told you about it."

"I haven't read a book since the 'Robber Barons,' and that will probably be my last."

"OK, good bye. Ryan, wait. Did you talk with Mike?"

With a click, the dial tone sounds and he's gone.

She had violated her own rule. The call from Brickman asking her to handle a production problem was a perfect opportunity for an update on his progress with her stock offer. But the call ended with her promising to make a call to Gus in Ho Chi Minh City.

. . . .

It is a dismal, overcast morning as Jane walks down the Strand, past Charing Cross Station, and into Bookers, at the corner with Whitehall.

"Triple Seven, please." She's dying for a cigarette, and though none of the UK brands taste right, 777 comes close enough. "And matches?"

Stepping back out onto the Strand sidewalk, she fidgets with the plastic film on the cigarette box, yanks one from the pack, and slides open the box of stick matches. The label on the box reads "Sure-Strike," with a picture of a bowling ball hitting three pins that are tumbling out of the picture. She cups her hands around the flame and draws her first smoke in 24 hours. She continues walking south towards Westminster and pulls her red cashmere scarf up around her neck.

Taking her Blackberry out for the call to Gus, she gazes across Cockspur Street to Churchill's statue in the square beyond, and, after a routine glance to the left for traffic, steps into the street against the light. A loud horn-blast nearly blows her backwards, followed by the wounded-beast scream of massive, split-rimmed wheels tearing into cold black top. As she turns to her right she just catches the terrified face of the driver through the picture-window windshield of the giant tour bus with a unfurling Union Jack graphic emblazoned on its flanks. The post-card picture of Winnie's statue in her field of view is instantly erased by the huge blue and red fender. She feels the engine's heat. She smells burning diesel. And she instantly raises her arms as the bus lunges toward her. Her full body — arms, chest, hips, and right thigh — are slammed at once, then at once recoil as the tires dig deeply into Cockspur Street.

She stands dazed, and her phone slides from her hand to the pavement. In the time it takes for her to clear her eyes from the adrenaline over dose, the driver leaps from the bus and takes Jane tenderly by the arm.

"My God girl, are you alright?" He looks terrified.

Remarkably, the choreography of the strike stayed precisely on the jagged edge of true disaster. Had she stepped a split second later, had the bus's velocity or weight been greater, who knows what would have happened. A little more forward momentum, a little less twist of fate, and where would she be now?

Assuring the driver, she picks up her Blackberry, walks carefully across to the statue and takes a seat with her back to Parliament.

Her heart is still pounding, but she forces herself to focus back on task. What was it that she was about to do prior to the crossing?

"Right. My phone. Call Gus in Ho Chi Minh City. That's it. Ryan said to call Gus."

She looks up Churchill's face, his jaw thrust down and forward in resolution, his eyebrow raised in argument at Parliament. She punches the send button on her phone. "Gus, what time is it there?"

"It's 18:00. Look Jane, I'm concerned about us changing the spec on the Hoffman product. I know that this seemed like a good idea when you were here last month. But if you remember your original trip, these guys were very particular about the spec. We'll have a couple of million dollars packed up before they ever see this stuff. What happens if they pull out? And on top of that, this is A-grade Russian crab, so who knows what we can expect in terms of uniformity?"

"Gus, I've had kind of a rough day. Look, it's dinner time there. Go home have a JW-Green with Amporn, and relax. This will be the best product they've ever seen. Once the customers buy it they'll start demanding it, and then we'll be the only ones with the manufacturing processes to make it. We'll crush Tongbang Brothers with this product, and frankly, there's nothing in the written spec that tells us we can't make this change, especially if it is super-spec. We're covered. Don't worry."

"Look Jane, it's not about what we want. It's about what
Hoffman wants. What their customers want. And they don't
want surprises."

"Gus, I have another call coming in that I've been waiting for. Can
we talk later? Just go with it. After all, this was your idea, right?
Talk to you tomorrow."

CHAPTER 6

Ryan Brickman slowly unfolds his long frame from the passenger side of the beat-up navy blue International pick-up. It's Noon in October in Dutch Harbor, and the sun is barely above the horizon. He squints at the light cutting between the plant and the "Akna R. Chernoff," a repurposed Liberty ship that now serves as Seven Seas' primary king crab processing factory.

. . . .

Brickman, Art Lesterman, who is the vice president over all of Seven Seas' production facilities, and Tom Bibby, manager of the Columbia River salmon plant, had been enjoying dinner the night before at the Red Lion in Astoria when Lesterman's cell phone registered a sequence of three pairs of gentle vibrations, each pair spaced a few minutes apart. Ryan hates being interrupted by cell phone calls at meals, and typically he insists that his people put them on "stun," or "better yet, turn the damn things off!"

It was the repeated pattern of three calls in a row that alarmed Lesterman. Maybe it's something wrong at home, he thought. He had excused himself, rose from the table, and headed into the bar, drawing the phone from his belt holster. Two "Missed Call" messages glowed on the screen, both from Akna Chernoff. The third was a text message: "Code Black. Call now."

Chernoff is a Russian-Inuit who grew up in the Alaskan fishery. His mother named him Akna, meaning "is rich," and his father baptized him into the salmon business soon after his 14th birthday, putting him to work in the receiving area of the cannery at the height of the sockeye run. His father was general manager of the Kenai plant, which was owned by the New England Fish Company. He was regarded as the most knowledgeable man in the company when it came to the art of managing the logistical maelstrom of processing three million pounds of sockeye — nearly 7,000 fish — per day over the course of the five-week early "Red Salmon" run up the Kenai River.

Akna had begun his apprenticeship by tossing whole fish onto a belt that fed the "Iron Chink," a Rube Goldberg contraption of gears and blades that automatically beheaded and gutted the fish as they came from the iced delivery tenders working the traps and the boats up and down the run.

It was during a breakdown at the height of the run in 1964 that Akna lost the three middle fingers of his right hand as he struggled to manually loosen the seized fly wheel that powered the contraption's three pairs of guillotine blades. His hand served as a permanent reminder to every man he met of the heightened level of risk that was simply a way of life in Alaska.

Cradling the phone between his thumb and pinky, he punches the incoming call from Lesterman.

"Art, it's bad news. We've lost the boats."

"Akna, what are you talking . . ."

"The Coast Guard found both of them capsized not a hundred yards apart, 118 miles out of Dutch, just west of the Pribiloff's."

"The crews?"

"No survivors. They're looking now, but there's no chance. If there was time to suit-up, they would have found them by now. If not, they were finished in ten minutes."

"What about a May Day?"

Lesterman was just coming to grips with the potential loss. Thirteen men, total. Mel and Nils Karensen had been recruited by Brickman during a trip to Iceland last June. The brothers were high-liner snow-crab fishermen out of St. John's. They had jumped at the chance to work for Brickman in the off-season. Skippering for Bering Sea king crab could more than double their usual crab earnings. Lesterman had grown fond of the Icelanders, and was aware that both had young families back in Reykjavik.

Chernoff had handpicked the crews, enlisted mainly through his connections in Anchorage and Seattle. There was one important exception: Todd Christian, son of Newday executive Carl Christian. Dreyfus was personally involved in arranging the position, with Brickman's blessing. This was their first trip out of Dutch Harbor with the brothers as skippers of Seven Seas' newest crabbers, the sister ships SIRIUS and VEGA. The boats were state-of-the-art fishing vessels with an innovative hull design and engineering that nearly doubled their operating efficiency during the deployment and recovery of the crab pots. Lesterman had fought hard for the $7,000,000 capital construction investment. The rising crab market and the weakening greenback finally convinced Brickman that the gamble was likely to payoff, and big. If the season worked, they could pay for the boats before New Year's.

"Nothing from either boat. No May Day, no emergency beacon. Last word was about 11 hours ago. Art, I've been in this business all my life and this is the worst ever. Coast Guard is blaming the pots. Maybe the boys hadn't balanced for the extra weight of the pots on the deck. Maybe they just weren't balanced. Maybe they were overloaded. Maybe somebody misread the displacement. But I can't believe it. Not both boats at once. It's got to be something else. Maybe a rogue wave."

Lesterman returned to the table to report the situation to Brickman, who immediately called Chernoff for a recap. After the call, as they slowly finished their meals, Brickman outlined a plan for the next few days.

By the time he would arrive in Dutch Harbor, Brickman would need the contact information for the next of kin of the crew members. He would make the Karensen and Christian calls, and divide the rest of the calls with Chernoff. He would head straight to Dutch in the morning.

Meanwhile, Lesterman would head to Seattle and organize meetings with the bank, the insurance company, and the attorney in time for Brickman's arrival in Dutch on Thursday morning.

"Listen Art, we need to make these calls as soon as possible after I arrive in Dutch. I don't want to get into a beef with the Coast Guard about notification. So get hold of the lawyer, Mike Molinari in Seattle, tonight. Ask him to pull the agreements. In the morning, I'll need a summary of what I can say and not say to the families. I know we've insured these guys, right? And what about the boats. Find out the details of the coverage, and let me know."

"Five hundred thousand each on the crew, one million each on Mel and Nils."

"Call the travel agent about arrangements for getting the families to Seattle. Spare no expense. I'll call you when I get to Dutch."

. . . .

And now Brickman is in Dutch, and it is up to him to make sure there is a personal conversation with the families of each and every one of the crew.

☙

CHAPTER 7

Jane's phone rings as she hangs up from Gus.

"David?" She is crossing the courtyard in front of Westminster Abbey, scanning the marble saints that frame the entrance.

"Jane, is this a good time? I just made it to my room and wanted to return your call. Sorry for the delay, but I had a client-call to make before calling you back."

"Perfect timing. If you don't mind, I need to ask you something, because it's been bothering me. When we were on the plane, you mentioned the importance of relationships. I told you that I did a lot to build relationships — all I can, in fact, to make personal connections. But frankly, it's not working. In fact, I'm beginning to feel like it's backfiring. It bothered me when we were talking, but I forgot to ask you. Must have been the Ambien!"

"Listen Jane, I'm sorry, but I only have a few minutes. Can you be more specific?"

"Last April, I was in Chicago at a big food conference. My biggest customer was there, with their whole buying staff. Let's just say they're one of the country's leading hotel chain operations, and very important buyers of our stuff. We've been a 'partner' — really a highly collaborative vendor — for some time. Low eight figures annually. I had arranged to have dinner at Lawry's Restaurant with the Senior VP, his number two, plus my boss. I get a call that morning from the VP's Admin advising me that the VP will be bringing his whole team, making it a party of 11. I naturally agree without checking with the restaurant, and I eventually manage to book 7:45 for the 11 of us. Now everybody's starving, and I'm sweating bullets. The wine bill alone promises to be a credit card buster . . ."

"Don't tell me. Great dinner. Everybody has a great time, and then they fire you."

"Yes, how did you know that? They fired us. I had done everything to build that relationship. I even let the vice president and his family use my vacation home for a week. And it got worse. Before they terminated us, they filed a claim — which they later dropped — then cancelled five orders worth more than $400,000. Strange thing is, as I was paying the bill I had a sinking feeling that something was wrong. I just couldn't put my finger it. Then, three weeks later, they dropped the bomb! So . . ., so much for my faith in relationships."

"Jane, I'm sorry I don't have the time to go into this in more detail right now, but I'd like you to consider this: I did more to establish a relationship with you by accidentally, on purpose, spilling my drink on your seat on the plane than you did spending a thousand bucks on your customer at Lawry's. Today, more than ever before, schmoozing doesn't matter if you haven't taken the time and energy to learn about what it is that is fundamentally important to your client's definition of success around your stuff. And the same holds for the person in authority who you have chosen to deal with at the client company. You need to think about their business priorities and their careers. If you haven't established a relationship that is centered on those questions first, then social-relationship building just doesn't matter. In fact, it can act in reverse. Because you've neglected the issues that are fundamentally important to the client in doing their job, they will become increasingly suspect of you and your motives. The same holds true for the traditional 'features-and-functions' thinking, or even 'the solution seller' who is focused on fitting their solution to the clients 'pain.' Sales people lose business in the long run because there is always a smart competitor out there who is willing to check their ego at the door, and discover what is going on from the client's side of the 'looking glass.'"

"David, you know what you are telling me here, don't you?"

"I know you've been selling like this your entire life. Don't feel bad. Most sales people have. Truth is, if you're working for an established 'brand,' it doesn't matter as much, because the skill of the salesperson doesn't matter as much. When people buy from Hewlett-Packard they're buying Dave Packard more than the HP sales person. They're buying the company. Its reputation. But if you are not 'the brand,' like most of us aren't, it's a whole different ballgame. You need to reach in and make a human connection. Create an important business relationship. Stop selling and start having real conversations with your prospects and clients."

CHAPTER 8

Brickman steps over the door sill leading to the original Captain's Stateroom on the old Liberty ship.

"You know A.C., I used to walk these same gangways in the South Pacific. Thank God the Japs didn't have the sub fleet that the Germans had."

The two men are seated on opposite sides of a square Navy surplus table, amidships behind the wheelhouse. The lawyer has written them a script to follow on the telephone calls, but it sits on the corner of the desk unopened. They had agreed to alternate calls to help lower the stress and take advantage of any insights they might gain and could share with each other. Protocol dictated starting the calls with the brothers' families, and, being native Icelanders, the law office had arranged a conference call through an interpreter at the Icelandic consulate in Seattle.

"Mr. Brickman, this is Mr. Merfynsson, the Consulate General for Iceland in Seattle. I am a not professional interpreter, but I have been briefed on the call and felt, considering the tragedy . . ."

"I understand. Thank-you. Oh, Mr. Murphy?"

"That's Merfynsson."

"Yes. Have you ever done this before — translated a call of this sort? About a death I mean?"

"No sir, this is the first time. Mr. Brickman, you should know that your Coast Guard requested that, because the brothers were foreign nationals working in the U.S., the Icelandic State Department should take over responsibility for notifying the families immediately, before it showed up in the press. Both of the Karensen wives were advised of the accident this morning. They understand that we are formally in the search-and-rescue period, but we've made it clear that the chance of finding survivors is very small. Nils' wife, Agee, understands English well, and can speak it a little. Mel's wife doesn't speak English at all, and will rely on Agee to interpret for her."

"Mrs. Karensen, this is Mr. Merfynsson from the Icelandic Consulate in Seattle. I have with me Mr. Ryan Brickman, President of Seven Seas, Inc., the owner of the fishing boat VEGA."

Icelanders are congenitally steeled to the dangers of fishing. Millennia of trawling and seining for cod in the seas between Greenland and Georges Banks have imprinted the Norsemen of this frozen enclave with resolute respect for the bounty that is both given and taken by the gray north Atlantic. Some historians measure the progress of western civilization by the development of this fishery and the Iberian, Nordic, and Anglo seafarers who have given their lives attempting to control it. Agee Karensen is of that stock, and her low, unwavering voice sounds worn from years of countless nights tending children and wrestling with the uncertainty of the lives she cherishes so far out at sea.

The brief exchange, in sober tones, is mostly business. No tears, no trip to recover the bodies. She knows that bodies are seldom found after the initial recovery mission. Just another legendary family fable, welding the generations with tales of fathers/brothers/ grandfathers/uncles lost in the worst fishing sea tragedy to touch the fisheries in the east or west.

CHAPTER 9

Jane's plan is to take the train on Friday night to Paris, then Sunday morning to Brussels. The conference begins on Sunday with a brunch, and Jane is scheduled to make her presentation to the Icelandic bankers on Monday morning.

Brickman had shared his plan with Jane about securing additional sources of working capital for expanding the business. "All of a sudden, after 20 years of a daily battle for market and for customers, my real struggle became finding enough money to fuel the growth," he had said. "And it's been that way ever since. This business is a beast that runs itself as long as I keep feeding it cash, cash, and more cash."

He had spoken about taking Seven Seas public, a first for a U.S.-based company solely in the seafood business. He had looked into bond funding of the cap-ex projects, and conserving cash for use inventories and receivables. But he'd finally decided that, regardless of the share price of a public offering, he could never personally tolerate sharing control of Seven Seas with a bunch of grumbling stockholders. And bond investors would demand convertibility, which, to him, was, likewise, unacceptable.

It was his baby and his management formula that had made Seven Seas great.

So Jane's trip was part of the hunt for the best deal Seven Seas could find for working capital. If Jane's presentation made Seven Seas' business prospects appealing enough for Islandbanc to make a proposal, Brickman was characteristically prepared to squeeze them for every possible concession he could get.

He knows that Iceland is loaded with cash, and that it all sits in the banks. Wealthy investors on the hunt for return on capital stumbled on Reykjavik as one of the high-yield flavors of the year. Icelandic fund managers had seduced U.S. and European Union bankers to throw in with them. Iceland, in a word, is "hot." It is burning money, and because Icelandic investors would assign a low-risk premium to seafood compared to the other "meat-eating" markets, Ryan figures that they might just have the cheapest money available to capitalize his plans for Seven Seas.

The front of the Pelham Hotel overlooks Cromwell Road and the South Kensington tube station. Jane is finishing a cigarette, waiting for Charles Earlsfield, as the classic, bottle-green Range Rover 3500 rolls quietly up to the curb from her right with a hushed rumble. Earlsfield's huge, bald, wire-rimmed head rises on his spindly frame from behind the wheel on the street side of the car. Earlsfield is Seven Seas' agent in the UK, and is responsible for delivering the handful of Hoffman stores the chain had managed to build in the wealthier suburbs of London.

Jane loves Charlie Earlsfield. He is the classic sincere salesman. He combines a dry, acerbic wit about people and markets with a genuine passion for the business. He can wax emotional when presenting to prospects about quality and value. It sounds corny sometimes, but it seems to work for him.

"Well, Jane, shall we sell some fish today? Or is this to be a social call?"

"Good day, mate. That's terrific. As usual, you've made an exception and are wearing a suit on my account. Quite nice of you to bother." The joke is that Earlsfield always dresses impeccably right down to a gold tie pin in the shape of a cod that suspends his green silk tie nattily in a dimple below his grotesquely bulging Adam's apple.

"Firstly, we don't say 'Good day' here in England. And secondly, unlike you Yanks, we consider ourselves to be professionals and always dress as such. Jane, listen, my office has been ringing me all morning. Brickman's been trying to reach you."

"Yes. Something in my voltage converter fried my Blackberry last night. I'll need to stop someplace to replace it."

"Frankly Janie, there's talk is that there's been some sort of accident in Alaska with a couple of the company's crab boats. Doesn't sound good, mate."

Speeding south on the M-5, the gravity of the situation slowly takes hold of Jane, draining from her all the novelty and joy of travel, of England, and of sparing with Charles.

Her telephone conversation with Brickman focused on Todd Christian. "I spoke with Carl at his home just after the Coast Guard called to notify the family of the accident, and let them know that the crew is missing and presumed dead. He's taking it hard. I could barely get a rational response. His wife is inconsolable. I need you to meet me in Denver on Wednesday afternoon. I have Doug making the arrangements to get you there from Brussels. Sorry kid, but duty calls."

Jane fills Charlie in on the details, including how she had made arrangements for Todd Christian to join the VEGA in Dutch Harbor, and how she had discussed with Carl Christian that crewing for king crab could be dangerous business, especially for a college kid. Christian had told her that "the boy needs that kind of experience to get him grounded." Brickman had fought the idea, fearing that just such an outcome could jeopardize one of their largest accounts. "Just pay the kid the money and stick him somewhere up in Seattle," the father had said.

But Jane sensed that, for once, Christian's commitment was more than just monetary. "Send him out there for a ride and put him to work. He needs it."

Jane had viewed the situation as a unique opportunity to strengthen Seven Seas' relationship with Christian and with Newday, and had assured the father, and reassured son Carl that the VEGA was brand new — a state-of-the-art boat with the latest safety systems and survival technology. Even if something went horribly wrong, there were redundant communications systems. It would be virtually impossible to lose contact with the Coast Guard.

Nils Karensen was a highliner, a world-class fishing boat captain with two decades of skippering in the North Atlantic, which was known for storms that could literally twist a ship in half. "Pacific" meant peaceful and calm to him. This experience was to be great for Todd Christian and ultimately great for Seven Seas.

For once, her sales pitch had worked flawlessly, and now Brickman's uncanny talent for anticipating the eventual outcomes of his actions had been validated again.

Jane is distracted. She had thought that her tenure working in Alaska had prepared her emotionally for nearly any disaster that the sea could deliver. But this one was different. The fact that 13 crew members were gone, including the son of her most important customer, was nearly too much for her to fathom.

CHAPTER 10

"Look Charlie, I'm not sure I'm up for this meeting this morning. You've got the ball on this one. I'm playing the 'expert witness' today, all right? If you have questions about the crab fishery, or processing, or the Saigon plant, just go ahead and ask me. Otherwise I'm laying back. That OK?"

"Of course Jane, I understand."

"And Charlie, if I start rambling, just pull on your ear lobe. That'll be our signal that I should shut up and hand it back to you."

"Brilliant, mate. Not to worry. I actually e-mailed Nigel yesterday with an agenda for this morning's meeting, so he'll be prepared for the conversation. I put a copy for you in the folder, in the door pocket. Have a look before we go in, if you like."

To: Nigel Howard, Hoffman, UK

From: Charles Earlsfield, Seven Seas, UK Dear Nigel,

The following is a suggested outline for our meeting with Jane Dreyfus at 10:00 on the morning of the 21st. Please advise your changes or additions to this agenda.

The memo went on to explain that the purpose of the meeting was to investigate Hoffman-UK's merchandising plan around seafood, in general, and king crab, in particular. They were interested in hearing the specific outcomes that Nigel Howard was seeking within the category. And, if the decision was made to proceed, what were his thoughts about what Seven Seas could do to contribute to the success of the merchandising program? The memo also suggested that the parties discuss high-level questions regarding the logistical and packaging needs of the U.K. stores, and gain some awareness of friction points in the system that could affect costing. Further, the memo suggested, the discussion would last about 45 minutes, with an outcome of an agreement whether or not to time line the product into the stores, and a decision on an absolute "Go/No-go" date.

"Charlie?" Jane turns her head to the right while holding up the red file folder in her right hand. "I'm sorry. Maybe I misread something. First, I think this is a good idea, so thanks for sending it out in advance so Nigel is oriented. But I'm curious. Do you always send an agenda like this ahead of your meetings? And second, I'm concerned with the details. There's nothing in here about us presenting our stuff. You know, our standard presentation, 'Seven Seas is the largest seafood producer in the Pacific Northwest with more than 25 years . . . blah, blah, blah.' And what about samples? You've got samples and the presentation with you, right?"

"Well . . ." Charlie paused. "Well, no actually I don't."

"You don't have the samples? Or the presentation? Charlie, I had them air-freighted from Seattle specifically for this meeting. And

I worked on the presentation for five hours. Did something go wrong in customs?"

"No, I just decided not to bring them."

"Are you out of your mind? Nobody goes to a food sales meeting without samples."

"Don't worry, Jane. Nigel will see the samples, but at the right time."

"Those sample cases have the brochures with the whole Alaska story. Christ, Charlie, the state of Alaska spends millions developing all of this sales stuff for use with overseas customers. They even changed it to sound more British and less American."

"Jane, I'm going to ask you for a favor. I'd like you to trust me on this one. I'm planning a different kind of sales conversation with Nigel than you are used to hearing. But it will result in a deal decision in half the time and with a fraction of the effort than it would have using that tired, old — what do you Yanks call it? — 'dog and pony show?'"

"Charlie, you picked a bad day to spring this kind of thing on me. We've only got 17 minutes until we're expected inside. If you had told me all of this earlier, I would have cancelled the meeting, especially in view of how this day has gone for me so far. I have never entered a prospect meeting without a presentation in hand, or a PowerPoint. And always samples."

Jane opens the Rover's door and steps out, then reaches into the back seat for her coat and scarf. She pulls a single 777 from the box and continues her rant, while pointing at Charlie with the lit end of match before it burned out between her fingers.

"Shit."

"Come on, Janie, I know this hasn't been the best morning for you. But the meeting will go fine. I promise. Best fish 'n' chips in London and a pint on me after we finish up with Nigel. Then you'll have the rest of the day off."

"Charlie, if we blow this account, there will be hell to pay. I promise you."

CHAPTER 11

Nigel Howard steps from behind his desk and walks over to the small circular table by the window overlooking the Hoffman-UK campus. As Vice President of UK operations, it's been a difficult year. Portland has had him on a very steep growth plan for same-store sales, and he's been tasked with opening one new store — and starting construction on another — over the next 18 months. The offices of Parliament members from the districts where the stores are being built have been pressing the company for campaign donations, and the local governments seem to come up almost daily with new regulations to leverage one more concession about street modification or neighborhood improvement. And now, corporate is foisting yet another doomed merchandising program, this time Alaskan king crab. Who the hell can afford £10 for a serving of crab with $100 barrel oil and UK unemployment nearing ten percent? Perhaps if he can actually make this all happen on cue, he'll be a cinch for the new VP of International Merchandising position that's about to open up in LA. He's always loved the States, and has been lobbying hard for the job since first learning about it during his June trip to Hoffman headquarters for their quarterly meeting.

He opens the door as Mary Smyth, Director of UK Merchandising, enters the office, followed by Tom Flowers, Director of Procurement. Smyth is a classic, dependable team player. She's proud of her ten-year service pin, and is very happy to be working for Howard. In fact, she is dedicated to his success. Though, at times, he seems tough, she respects his ability to make decisions and shoulder responsibility. Flowers is the check-list kind of guy, and Howard relies on him to handle the myriad details required to logistically get a product physically on a shelf. Flowers's fear of getting the details wrong verges on compulsion. But he is great at it, and can be counted on to bring an unbiased attention to detail to any project. Flowers is intimidated by Howard, but grateful for the praise he gets for his organizational skills and irrefutable numbers.

"Listen folks, we have the king crab fellow Charlie Earlsfield on the calendar this morning, and he's bringing Jane Dreyfus from Seven Seas, Alaska. It's a command performance from HQ. I'll be ducking out after a few minutes, but I want this deal in a permanent holding pattern. Look, it's an 11:00 meeting. Worst case, you both get taken to a free lunch."

"Nigel, we don't have the frozen space in the stores for the items we currently have in the ad for the holiday promotions," Mary says. "And I would barely have time to get this into the Christmas free-standing advert, even if we did have room. And even that assumes that there is ad copy ready to go, which there probably isn't. Plus, crab price points are horrendous in this kind of market."

"Mary, don't get your knickers in a pinch. This deal isn't going to happen. Plus, I've got it covered from our side. They don't have the quality or the price, so this meeting is going to be a typical time waster — them telling us all about the history of their company and of Alaskan king crab, then dumping out samples all over the place. I hope one of you likes crab."

Flowers nods his head towards Howard, his arms on the table and his shoulders low as if to share a secret. "I'll have them dancing like ballerinas. Her Majesty's Customs & Excise, plus the new EU food additives regulations, will have them thinking that U.S. FDA and Customs compliance is a bloody walk in the park. Plus, I have my own checklist to cover. I'll have them walking out smiling as usual, thinking that it was a brilliant sales meeting. All they need to do is fill out a few forms to get the order. This Jane woman will head back to the states beaming because she met with the "Hoffman-UK people," telling everyone how she dismantled us. She'll just sit back and wait to collect the orders. It's always the same — once they realize we've gone dark, we'll have to put up with their calls and e-mails. By the way, I suggest routing their messages to a separate folder or to junk, as usual. And Nigel, I've noticed that you occasionally answer your own phone line. I suggest you let it go to voice mail like I do, then you can just delete through your messages a couple of times a day. I really do get sick and tired of vendors who can't take a hint. You'd think by the tenth call they'd realize that there's no deal."

"OK, but play it carefully. This is a corporate deal, Tom. We need to acknowledge a call or e-mail once in a while or someone will start complaining to Stinball. But I want Seven Seas DOA. Understand? We've got Sid from Tongbang Brothers coming in on

Monday and I've already got a Russian crab deal lined up with him. So we just need to handle these folks so they think there's still a chance for the order, until it's just too late for them to ship, that is. I'll take care of you guys as usual."

Earlsfield and Jane arrive and are seated at a rectangular table with six plastic chairs in the small, stark-white conference room on the second floor of the tilt-up concrete Hoffman-UK Distribution Center, which doubles as their UK corporate offices. The floor rumbles with the rhythmic clang and diesel engines of the tow-motor lifts that back out of the vans after loading their pallets with merchandise. There's a gentle knock at the door, and it swings open to reveal Nigel Howard's moon-shaped face grinning ear-to-ear.

"Sir Charles, wonderful to see you again!"

Mary and Tom follow close behind. They both lack the power to say "Yes" to any vendor regarding placement of a product in Hoffman stores. Their power is to keep the options open. But in the end, only Howard can say "Yes." They can only say "No."

Earlsfield notices a binder under Tom's arm, perfectly tabbed and neatly labeled "Food Product Specifications." He makes Tom out as a "C Type" on the DISC personality scale[1], and mentally notes to keep the "altitude" low when talking with him. And to stick with the data, while being sure not to make any assertions that can't be backed up with data. In discussions with Tom he would need to be cautious about understanding exactly the answer Tom is looking for. And he would need to drill down until there was clarity on it.

Mary's fuzzy blue sweater and conservative schoolgirl plaid skirt and leggings signaled Earlsfield that she is probably an "S" on the DISC. She carries an insulated cup of tea and shares a relaxed smile with him as the group approaches the table.

With Mary he would need to be cautious, to guard against his own natural "I" tendency to be over exuberant, and often too quick and clever in his comments and observations. Earlsfield has a tendency to look for the humor in every situation, and he understands that this can be off-putting to certain personality types. With an "S" on the buying committee he will need to be friendly, yet careful, to avoid a polarizing topic that could cause Mary to become stubborn or even passive aggressive.

1   DISC is the name for a psychological inventory that classifies four aspects of human behavior by testing a person's preferences in word associations. DISC is the acronym for:

- **D**ominance – relating to control, power, and assertiveness

- **I**nfluence – relating to social situations and communication

- **S**teadiness – relating to patience, persistence, and thoughtfulness

- **C**ompliance – relating to structure and organization

Earlsfield and Jane rise to greet them. He is cordial, but Jane notices that he is unusually formal in his manner as he remains standing to introduce her. The others begin to sit, but they are forced to stand again as Earlsfield introduces each team member by name — facilitating the exchange of cards with Jane.

"We genuinely appreciate your inviting us in today, and we're excited at the prospect of doing business together. Nigel, may I ask you how you are fixed for time this morning?"

Howard is caught off guard with Earlsfield's question. He was hoping to slip out when there was a lull in the conversation, but now he will have to give Earlsfield a commitment on his time.

"Oh, I'd say what, 45 minutes should do it Charles, don't you think?"

"OK, that puts us at 11:45 to wrap up." Earlsfield sets his cell phone on the table, opened like an egg timer. "Also, Nigel, did you have a chance to read over the agenda I sent on Wednesday?"

Howard nods yes. "Here are copies for reference."

As Earlsfield puts his red folder back into his briefcase he turns to Howard. "I gather you were comfortable with the content, but please, feel free to let me know if there is anything you'd like to change or to add."

Howard's expression turns from a friendly grin to a pensive, but engaged, look of curiosity. This is not starting out like a typical sales call. He's becoming interested in exactly what Earlsfield has in mind for the rest of the meeting, because the brief conversation so far has been one-sided and gently controlling. Howard has been formally instructed in negotiations and dealing with vendors, and he knows that the smart strategy is always for the buyer to remain in control by whatever means necessary. Here, Earlsfield has taken the lead from the outset, and in such a comfortable manner that Howard feels unmotivated to interfere with the process.

"Jane arrived in London yesterday to meet with us. She is Senior VP of Sales for Seven Seas, Inc., the producer and distributor for the king crab program arranged by Paul Stinbell's team in Portland. Because she isn't real familiar with UK operations, I was hoping that we could begin the meeting with you folks telling her a bit about your roles in the process of getting the program going here, and what you each is hoping to learn from today's meeting."

Howard raises his chin abruptly above the horizontal, smiling slightly and casting his eyes to Smyth and Flowers on his right and left.

"Well Charles, not to sound ungrateful for Jane's visit — we are very happy to have her here — but frankly, we haven't decided, as yet, whether or not the Seven Seas program will work for Hoffman-UK customers. Having said that, I do have questions about how the program currently operates in the U.S., and what the numbers have been like so far."

Jane leans forward. "I have numbers as of last week. I can . . ." But Earlsfield reaches up and immediately pulls at his earlobe and gently interrupts. "Nigel, since you were good enough to invite us in for this meeting, I had reckoned that you had already spoken with Paul on this. Is it possible to get the most current sales numbers from the States from your own system?"

Earlsfield knows that Hoffman has an internal enterprise-resource planning system that allows local management to look up piece movement in any other part of the system, including foreign locations. If the numbers really are the issue, Howard finding them in his own organization is far better than Jane quoting them from her report.

"But I'm curious about your comment on why the Seven Seas program might not be the best for your customers. You must have good reason to believe there might be a problem, and I'd be interested in knowing your thoughts."

Howard is again intrigued with the redirection of his question. Earlsfield has preempted a typical sales BS answer with an obvious truth: There is no way Howard would have agreed to a conversation with them if he hadn't gotten a thumbs up from Paul in the U.S. Further, Hoffman's retail database is legendary. It can provide instantaneous, real-time data on the movement of chocolate-covered cockroaches in their store in Rancho Cucamonga. So the U.S. data on movement of Seven Seas crab is only a click away, and the Boston-area movement data is the best predictive tool on likely success of an item once it travels to the U.S. The line of conversation is little more than Earlsfield's recognition that Howard has nothing truly relevant to ask, and has led off with a meaningless "boiler plate" question.

But how did Earlsfield know? It took courage to take charge of the conversation and cut the real issue: Why does Howard think that UK shoppers will reject king crab for the holidays?

Howard knows from experience that sales people are typically professional hoop jumpers. When a buyer asks for numbers, sales people always grab for a file folder or they rifle through a presentation for the appropriate evidence to justify their position. Of course, the numbers are always naturally suspect, because no salesperson in their right mind is going to report bad numbers. Frankly, it's almost entertaining to watch "solution sellers" try to bend every issue and every objection to their advantage using facts and data about their stuff. It would be entertaining, that is, if it weren't such a bloody waste of time. But this conversation is different, and Howard wants to know where Earlsfield is headed.

Howard scrambles a bit, "Well, that's just to say that the program deserves a good look from all sides — operationally, that is, and from the customers' viewpoint. Mary, what is your thinking on how our shoppers will go with this program?"

Smyth, head of UK merchandising, is unprepared for this handoff. She's caught off guard. She had expected her boss to have gone for the kill by now, but he hasn't, and now he is tossing it to her as if he is actually considering the facts of the program.

"Well, from my vantage point in merchandising, I really don't see the "Three Ps" lining up for this product, especially for the holiday promotional calendar. Even if there is space, I need to know a lot more about what can be done about the price point, the promotional funds, couponing, and the like. We've never carried king crab, so we have no idea how our shoppers will respond to it. I need to know how the addition of this item is going to make things better here in terms of overall mix. And what about returns, rain checks, and protecting our downside if it doesn't sell at all? What sales guarantee goes with this?"

Earlsfield jumps in. "We guarantee that we will deliver the goods on time and in the condition, specification, and at the price as promised. In terms of selling it in the stores, we do not make any guarantee. Tell me Mary, does our lack of a guarantee kill the deal? If I cannot guarantee the sales in your stores, is our conversation over?"

Smyth gives every outward appearance of sliding into a debilitating anxiety attack. Her eyes are darting left and right with no particular focus. The blood has drained from her face, and, though she is trying to speak, her sentences keep snapping off once the subject is barely out of her mouth. She is fingering her service pin that's attached squarely at the breast level of her sweater.

"Thank you, Mary." As Earlsfield jots a few notes on the legal pad he turns to Flowers, the procurement director. "Tom, what about your side? What are your questions or concerns?"

"First of all, the price is too high. It won't work. Procurement is going to need at least three competitive bids for the same spec product. In fact, I suggest a formal Request for Proposal. And the specification is really critical on an item that's this expensive. I need to know that we're getting what we're paying for. Quality is huge to UK customers, more so than in the States. We also need to be very careful before we slot something from the U.S. After the disasters with Mad Cow and Avian Flu, we don't need any more issues with imported food products. Our management just won't have it. Our people want to test every box for contaminants before the product goes into the freezer case."

"OK," says Earlsfield, "so as I understand it, Tom, you have a checklist of items around price, logistics, and specification that need to be in order. You mentioned an RFP. How can I be of help for you to get this done?"

Requests for Proposals have become the bane of existence for salespeople, and Earlsfield and Jane are no exceptions. RFPs are not only unwinnable at the profitable margin, but, unless you, as the vendor, actually participated in writing the RFP, your chance of winning so low enough that the effort does not justify burning the resources needed to submit one. For years Earlsfield has spent countless hours, week after week, filing out the documents and boosting to his boss with a lot of hype about "Yes, and we're working that RFP from Walmart." In truth, most times, there was never a chance of winning. He should have known that when he couldn't even get the buyer on the phone to find out how he had qualified for the race to begin with. Truth be known, he had always been just another warm body to add legitimacy to the bidding process, but there was never a chance in hell. Worse yet, all of the information, including pricing, that he put into his RFPs had actually become free consulting information for the prospect, and often for the prospect's incumbent vendor, as well. Talk about double jeopardy. Is there anything worse than playing for the right to lose, while revealing critical information about sourcing, logistics, and product specs? The bottom line is that the combination of opportunity-cost, free consulting, and the psychic damage to the salesperson and organization every time another bid went dark is devastating. The only way it ever makes sense is if Earlsfield writes the RFP for the buyer. "The battle is won before it is fought." Earlsfield thinks it through with chuckle. Well, let's not disappoint old Tom.

"Tom, on your point about the RFP, I appreciate why you want one, and I respect the potential benefits to Hoffman. But candidly, unless you want me to write it with you so that we are guaranteed that I get it right — and I reckon that you don't want to do that — then we're not willing to participate in the RFP process."

Jane is panicked by the look of astonishment on the faces of the Hoffman team. Clearly no vendor has ever spoken to them like this. What the hell is Charlie up to?

Jane can stand it no more, and now jumps in, "Naturally we want to do anything we can to help you to . . . ."

Jane's voice fades as Earlsfield cuts in. "Please forgive me folks, but I'm a little confused. I hope you can help me to understand what we are doing here. You invited us in today on the basis of a rather unique, direct-sourced merchandising opportunity for Hoffman's holiday promotions. The item has already been successfully piloted in hundreds of stores in the U.S., for which you have excellent, current sales data. We are a hundred days away from the drop-dead "in-store" date, and you are talking about putting together an RFP for the 12 UK stores. Can you help me understand why it's appropriate to be discussing an RFP at this point?"

There is dead silence from the Hoffman side of the table, and, if this is possible, Jane is feeling an even deeper sense of dread than she did after Brickman's call, and when she learned that Earlsfield had no canned sales presentation prepared for their meeting.

Howard pushes his chair back from the table while looking at Flowers. Howard's face has changed from a cocky grin to one of calm thoughtfulness. His eyes are cast slightly downward, and his lower lip is pinched between his teeth as if he is trying to restrain himself from either an angry outburst or a laughing fit.

"Nigel, can you help me to this one. Why are we here today? What was it that either Paul or I said that encouraged you to support the worthwhile idea of arranging for the five of us to talk about your merchandising goals and how we might help you to achieve them."

"Charles, I have a lot of bombs ticking on my desk, and to tell you the truth, I intended to leave this meeting some time ago to get back to managing all of them. If I took the time to explain my business plan to every vendor I met, I'd never get anything done."

"I understand, Nigel. And I'm sure Tom and Mary probably agree that they planned on the outcome of this meeting to be something that mattered, something that makes a difference in the outcome of your business."

Smiling, Earlsfield turns to Jane. "After all, you folks ain't short of friends to talk to, right? It's not like you had nothing else to do this morning, so you said, 'OK, what the heck, let's waste an hour talking with that bald-headed fish guy and some crab woman just in from the States.'"

There is a barely audible laughter around the table. Then, even Howard can't resist the humor in the comment, and he lets go with a sequence of low guttural chuckles that roll up through his diaphragm and out his nose — as much snorting as laughing.

"Listen, Charles . . . and Jane. I've got some aggressive targets I need to hit with holiday sales, so it's all about the numbers. Mary will analyze the merchandising projections against our local benchmarks. This item has a high price point, but if the U.S. data shows us that we'll get better sales if we slot in the king crab in place of another item, then we'll do it."

Flowers turns abruptly to face Howard. "But, we need a competitive bid. And what about the specifications?"

"Charles, please get Tom together with your technical people to work out the logistical elements. Meanwhile, Mary, please get Charles access to the vendor-managed inventory system, and begin the process of filling in the item particulars. Jane, I doubt that you've seen one of our stores yet. Charles, drive Jane over to our new Hampstead store. It's opening tomorrow. I'll meet you there for your VIP tour."

Jane has done countless tours through retail stores in her life, and she is not treasuring another one. But she reminds herself that, after all, she's in England. This will be an opportunity to see a little different spin on retail seafood. One of the disappointments she is beginning to notice in retail is how every store, whether in San Francisco, Tokyo, Bangkok, Paris, or Kuala Lumpur, is beginning to look the same. Same displays, same packaging. Even the same fish. When she was a kid, fresh salmon was only available in a very limited number of major metropolitan markets. And even then, it was mainly there from June to September. She recalls how the stores anticipated the opening of the season, how every chef and butcher in San Francisco and Seattle was waiting for the first fish of the season. One year, during a particularly slow opening catch, she had seen two buyers from two of the exclusive clubs in San Francisco get into a gaff fight right in the middle of the fish market over the last box of salmon from that day's catch. It ended when one of them caught a hook deep into his left gluteus maximus.

Her "Thank you, Nigel, that would be terrific!" is pure method acting. Howard smiles at her with obvious pride at her interest in seeing their store.

"That's great. You'll love it. State of the art. Herb spared no expense on this one."

"Thank you, Nigel," says Earlsfield. "But before we go, I have a couple of questions. Very straight forward. Is that OK?"

Earlsfield pauses as all eyes turn his way, and Howard nods in agreement. He goes through his notes with a pen looking for anything he had noted as actionable. "You understand that we are offering this program exclusively to Hoffman here in the UK, so our timing is critical."

Then he begins his question, looking at Howard, but slowly turning his head toward Mary Smyth. "When will we know a decision regarding Mary's merchandising analysis?"

Smyth responds with, "You can call me next week, say Wednesday or Thursday." She has adopted a more deferential tone, and while she speaks, she keeps one eye on Howard.

"OK, are you comfortable with Thursday?," Earlsfield asks. "Are you sure that's enough time? If so, how about 9:45?"

Smyth agrees, and Earlsfield moves on. "This will sound like an odd question, but if I get your voice mail when I call, what message can I leave you to assure me that you will call me back, but won't make you angry?"

"I'm usually very busy at that time of the morning," Smyth says, "so if you miss me just wait a few minutes and try calling me back."

"I understand. Maybe there's a better time then?" Earlsfield pauses, but no answer is forthcoming from her. She squirms in her chair and looks at Howard.

"Listen Mary," Earlsfield is firm but friendly. "I know that you have the best of intentions, but the time just gets away from us these days. I'm sure you understand that calling back can easily turn into an endless tail-chasing exercise that I'd rather avoid."

"Just call me Thursday, at 9:45. We'll eventually connect."

"Mary, I'm sorry, but I have a problem with that. You see, I don't . . . call back."

Howard intervenes. "Charles, don't worry. Send Mary an appointment invitation. If you don't get Mary at the 9:45 appointment, leave her a message. I promise you that we'll return your call within a half hour. If that doesn't work, call me."

"Thanks, Nigel. One last thing . . ."

Howard chuckles, and the others reluctantly join in. "Good grief Charles, can we finish? I as much told you. Let's get on with it."

"I know, and I appreciate that. But you'll be needing to talk about it obviously. And I'd like to say that if you are looking at, say, a mid-November arrival — not that you are, but just supposing, for logistics sake, it takes 60 days — today we're here in the first week of September, so all I am saying is, if you decide after your meeting that this is a 'No Go,' would you do me a favor?"

Howard purses his lips and nods his head in agreement.

"Just tell me. That's my only demand. Neither you nor I gain by keeping a secret. That's what causes train wrecks. If we suddenly can't make these shipments for one reason or another, I will call you right away with the bad news. Likewise, if you should decide that this promotion is not a fit, hold up your hand and it's over. Fair enough?"

"Candidly, Charles, I've pulled out of plenty of deals that weren't measuring up on vendor performance or unit movement. In fact, I pride myself on adherence to the numbers. But, I've never had a vendor walk away from business with me. Well, with Hoffman that is."

"Great. Well then, thank you for inviting us to visit with you. We are very excited at the prospect of doing business with you. We'll see you at Hampstead in, say, one hour?"

"Charlie, what the hell was that all about?" Jane is still buzzing with disbelief with the conversation she just observed.

"Sorry mate. What exactly didn't you understand?"

"The whole thing. What all those questions about returning the call, for example. Were you just trying to aggravate these people?"

"Jane, I'm not going to fight these accounts. This is business. You need to be deliberate. Either we get down to reality and figure out why we're sitting together talking, or we decide to stop. As business people we need funds, not friends."

"Yes, but why press the point. She said that 9:45 was a good time. Why not just say, 'OK, put it on your calendar,' and leave it at that?"

"Jane, it's not about the phone call."

"I'm sorry, now you've really lost me."

"I've accomplished at least three important things by pressing the point about the call. One, I've set the expectation that when I make an appointment I expect it to be met. I am not going to chase a retail buyer, trying to get a straight decision on some merchandising analysis that both of us, by the way, already know the answer to."

Jane is jet lagged. Her emotionally exhausting day is beginning to take a toll on her brain. "Expectation." Where have I heard that before?

"Charlie, I need some coffee." He exits east off the M-25 toward Chatham as Jane tilts the seat back and cracks the window. The cool sea air rushes in, mixing with the warmth of the Rover's heater, but it's refreshing to her none the less. She can smell the sea.

"The Café Rouge is near the Hampstead store. Can you make it 15 minutes more for your caffeine?"

Without waiting for an answer, Earlsfield continues, "The second thing is that I am qualifying the account. I'm not trying to qualify me to them. If they aren't professional enough to return a call that's been pre-scheduled, are they really the kind of business people that I want to be doing business with?"

"Charlie, get serious!" Jane's irritation is obvious. "Look, this is a $45 million account, end-to-end, right."

He nods in agreement.

"And you're telling me that this is about them qualifying for us for Christ sake! Who the hell are we? We aren't even on their radar. They don't need us. I've been chasing this account for years. I need them, not the other way around. And now you're telling me that they need to qualify for us?"

"Jane, this is not about need. This is about control. Self-control. Controlling the sales process, and having the self-esteem to reject living in the perpetual sales purgatory of 'When are they going to call me? When are they going to reply to my e-mail?' Just like — and pardon me for saying this, but — a 14-year-old girl! I'm just not going to live there. I have the right to put my own constraints on the way I do business. I'm not going where I'm not needed. I *am* going to find that out as early, efficiently, and empathetically as possible, so I don't get over invested in an account where there's little or no future. Every single account is the same to me, big or small. I'm not getting emotionally enthralled with an account because they are big and might mean a lot of business, or dismissive if they are small and don't buy much. I'm not comfortable with that valuation of my business. I'm enthralled if they need me, if they need to buy my stuff. And by the way, Jane, it's also about options. By the way, we'll be stopping off for a 2 o'clock with my current 'victim.'"

CHAPTER 12

"Hello, this is Og Johannson, with Iceland Bancshares. I'm trying to reach Mr. Brickman, please."

Mike Molinari's law office is on the 21st floor of the Dollar Building, overlooking Pioneer Square in downtown Seattle. Ryan Brickman squints against the afternoon sun hanging over Puget Sound. Yesterday's production numbers are down substantially, as expected, with the loss of the two boats. But his concerns go beyond the immediate issues to what could be, and would be, done to get the production numbers up to a price that will allow him to profitably fulfill the orders that the company has booked for the holiday season. This is the largest roll of the dice he's made on the U.S. retail market, but he decided last season that he was sick and tired of being under the thumb of the Japanese crab buyers.

For years Japan has dominated the global king crab trade. They fly in to Dutch Harbor and Kenai and Seattle with suitcases full of cash — like they owned the place. The over-concentration of king crab purchases by the Japanese means that they are able to dictate the price during any given season. Seven Seas is Alaska's biggest crab packer, and that makes Ryan Brickman the first stop every October for the annual Japanese buying tour. But

Brickman has become weary of the prevailing attitude among the producers that whatever the big Japanese store chains — Ito Yokado, Mitsukoshi, and the like — decide to pay for crab is the global market's benchmark. And he has to like it. It's not that the price isn't profitable. With the slowly strengthening Yen, he has been making windfall profits from the "Red" king crab. But over the past few seasons he has experimented with various methods of breaking the Japanese's intimidating approach to negotiating price, and this year he'll use his most bold and dramatic plan yet. It still makes him laugh to think about the preparations he has made for their arrival.

Early in the summer, Brickman had put Jane to work booking U.S. retail crab promotions for the year-end holidays. He wanted to target every major merchandiser who could afford to have the $19.99 price point in their seafood counters. Jane managed to arrange a package of national and regional promotional commitments for one quarter of the projected pack, and had booked an equal amount of Russian king crab on promo as a hedge against short U.S. supplies.

The Seven Seas master agent in Asia is Gus Jambon. He has contracted for repacking the Russian product slightly underweight for U.S. retail in a new state-of-the-art duty-free freezer facility in a the Free Trade Zone in Saigon harbor. If they were caught by U.S. customs, they could claim it was the packing factory's fault, so long as nothing in the documentation indicated that the goods were being packed underweight.

Typically, the Japanese buying team would come into the office, exchange formalities, and then hand Brickman a market order with the price and tonnage they wanted. He fought them every year in an escalating battle for higher numbers, but any gains were incremental, at best, and he would always relent to their demands. But not this year. Now Seven Seas had the orders to back up their price demands, and when those "little bastards" starting squeezing his balls, threatening to cut him out, Brickman was prepared to give them the axe!

"Mr. Brickman?" The soft, clipped aristocratic tone of Mike Molinari's redheaded assistant, Marsha, interrupts the Japan king crab tragedy playing out in his mental opera house. "Mr. Johannson is on the phone for you from Iceland."

She leads him to a private conference room, past a gallery of nouveau bullshit artwork that seemed, to him anyway, a supreme waste of good wooden paneling. He enjoys the perfect cadence of her high heels doing alternating push-ups under her herringbone skirt.

"I'll send in the call in just a moment, Mr. Brickman. Just hit the flashing button and pick-up the receiver."

"Ryan, I couldn't raise you on your cell phone."

"Where are we on this deal, Og? I hope you've gotten these fellows lined up for Jane."

"Yeah, no problem. Ryan, I took the board members out to dinner at the Grand Place last night. You know, the standard night of chest thumping, Icelandic style. Then I took them to Noctis, which is this amazing club — kind of Cirque du Soleil Erotique.

This one is going to cost you Ryan. I spent 1,000 euros on these guys."

"If they come through with the deal, it won't matter. If they don't, I'm going to kick your ass, and you know that's not just a threat."

Johannson has heard stories about Brickman's potential for exploding when business doesn't go according to his plan. One of the more infamous stories was told to him by Frank Barrow, one of the "Klondike Crew": One year, when the Seven Seas management team was in Alaska for the opening of the sockeye salmon fishery, Barrow had been meeting with Brickman in his Kenai office. A radio message came in that one of the Seven Seas buying tenders moored in Cook Inlet had begun buying sockeye from the fishing boats, even though Brickman had yet to issue his market order or give his command to start buying. Boats were pulling up to the tender clamoring to unload, and the inexperienced buyer running the barge caved in and began buying at $2.65 a pound. It was the best spot price he could negotiate, but it was also a full 25 cents above the number Brickman planned to pay for the 20 million pounds that would be tendered over the coming weeks. Brickman called for his helicopter and ordered Barrow to join him on the ride out to the tender. During the 15-minute flight Brickman calmly reviewed last-minute details for the provisioning the four plants and thousands of employees who were needed to support the six-week salmon marathon that was going to begin at any moment.

"Set us down in the middle of the deck. Now!" The pilot tightened his banking maneuver around the barge's stern while below, a small cluster of men, their hats pressed down against the rotorwash, approached the landing area. As the chopper came to rest, Brickman, who never wears a safety belt, jumped out of the chopper, and, after five long strides, grabbed the jacket collar of the front man, and gave him a round house punch to the jaw that lifted him to his heels and sent him reeling backward into the arms of one of his cohort.

"You son-of-a-bitch. You just cost me $5 million bucks!", punctuating "bucks" with another lunge at the visibly terrified manager. "Get the hell off this barge before I kill you." As the story goes, Barrow and the pilot rushed in to restrain Brickman, but not before the station manager had literally jumped overboard into the icy north Pacific waters to avoid Brickman's next assault.

"Ryan, this is a done deal, I tell you. The board is with us. They're mainly Iceland fish C-Suite. A couple of them were in the states during the summer and saw your new slots and packaging in the Hoffman stores. They're sick and tired of the commodity cod business. They're always fighting over here, no retail branding. It's, as we say, 'When everybody's pissing in the same corner, pretty soon it starts to stink.' No profits! I wouldn't be surprised if one of them comes in and asks to buy Seven Seas. I'm serious. And the bank is prepared to back 'em. There's been a terrific flow of U.S. dollar investments into Reykjavik ever since the James Bond movie was made here. The bank needs to move it back out and what better way than to buy a U.S. seafood company."

"Listen Og, I'm looking for needed working capital to cover this retail. I need that capital at the best rate I can get. That's it. I'm not interested in selling the company. Just get me a $100 million asset-based line at Libor[1] minus 1.25 and I'll be happy."

"First, forget that rate. It won't happen. Maybe a minus .75, and even that's a stretch." Johannson pauses and sighs. There is a palpable change in his mood and an audible darkness now to his dead calm voice. "Yeah, yeah, Ryan. The food business is good right now, I understand. But we're not in the food business. We're not farmers or ranchers or corn flake makers. As you've learned dearly this week, this is a business of sea and wind. Things can change in an instant and suddenly 13 men are dead. You need to expect the unexpected because it is the nature of our crazy existence. I'm just telling you about the conditions right now. They are perfect to sell, but I guarantee you that it will change, and fast. But if you want, you can take advantage of it. It's up to you."

Brickman changes the subject. He knows instinctively that Johannson is right. It's the law of "buy low/sell high." As his mentor Jack DeLucia once told him, "If you want something to hold in a hot market, hold a beautiful woman. But when a market is high and pointing up, it's time to sell, sell, sell."

"Ryan the wild card is Hella Elgar, the new senior VP of asset-based lending. I have never met her, but I hear that she is tough. That's all I know."

"Og, Jane Dreyfus is in London right now. She'll handle the presentation to the bank. She's the architect of the business with Hoffman and a number of our other accounts. She's staying at the

---

1 Libor (**L**ondon **I**nterbank **O**ffered **R**ate) is the average interest rate that leading banks in London charge when lending to other banks.

Metropolitan and arrives tomorrow. You'll get an e-mail with all the details."

"Mr. Brickman, Mr. Molinari will see you now."

Brickman hangs up the phone without saying good-bye, and stares out the conference room window at the hundreds of boats and ships navigating Puget Sound 500 feet below him. His gut has suddenly become knotted, always a predictor for him that something important is about to change. That something has gone on too long. He is going to be forced — out of the necessity to survive — to make some tough decisions that will change everything for him and his team. And, as usual, he has to drag them all, kicking and screaming, into the next great adventure. All of them but Jane, of course. She is the one member of the pack who is always game for a new hunt, for new frontiers.

Brickman has known Molinari since high school. He was always a pretentious punk kid, the kind you wanted to haul off and punch, just for his obnoxious attitude. But he is a good lawyer, and has managed to get Seven Seas out of a couple of serious jams over their 22-year relationship. One of the most recent involved a wrongful-death lawsuit.

· · · · · · ·

Joe Barentino owned a small fish company in the San Francisco fish alley, and was heavily invested in the Japanese herring roe business. San Francisco herring eggs are prized by the Japanese for their size and flavor, and each spring, when the roe-laden herring return to the bay, Japanese buyers descend on the Golden Gate.

The key for any packer to make a killing in this *"ikura"* is to pay the right price, meaning low. Brickman hated to over pay for anything, and was known for his thoroughly anti-trust, midnight telephone tirades to competitors who dared to start buying from the fishermen at a price that didn't add up to his arithmetic. By the spring of 2002, he had grown tired of just breaking even on ikura, and he hatched a plan to fix his competitors for good. He would float a rumor of a high price into the market early, and start right out of the gate buying aggressively for 10 days. Once he started, herd instinct would kick in. The others, especially Barentino, would think he had inside info on the market and would begin buying aggressively, as well, driving the price even higher in an effort to cut Brickman off. And he would let them. Brickman also planned to fake a fire at his largest buying station at Point Reyes so it would have to shut down just as the run and the price were peaking. Brickman did have inside information, and it was that the herring run was cyclical, and that the Bay was well overdue for a bumper crop of ikura. The cycling nature of markets was not well understood by his competitors, but to Brickman it was a religion. Many people in the industry were enthralled with his uncanny ability to anticipate the future. Barentino, in particular, had been an arch rival of Seven Seas, and his ego in playing various fisheries markets had nearly cost him the company a number of times. But when it came to San Francisco Bay ikura, Barentino fancied himself as the "Herring King," having been ferried to Tokyo every other year by Japan's biggest buyers, Nissoho and Daichi Umi, for a libidinous romp through the *Ginza* to curry his favor for the next herring season.

The 2002 season began weakly, playing perfectly into Brickman's gambit. He opened his three buying stations full throttle, paying more than $4,300 per ton for the egg-laden herring (and in cash rather than company checks), while giving free beer, cigarettes, and provisions to any boat delivering to the Seven Seas docks. Other companies initially refused to pay the 15 percent premium, and Seven Seas took in 100 percent of the meager catch that the fleet delivered. With increased effort, the tonnage began to increase slowly, and the pressure on Barentino to step in and buy was more than he could resist. He opened all four of his stations and issued orders to begin buying at two percent over Seven Seas, then three percent. But still he received no deliveries. Brickman was monitoring Barentino's radio broadcasts to the boats and matching him dollar-for-dollar with each raise. Other packers dotting the bay also decided that the season was slipping away and raised the ante for the game. Barentino shifted to "open pricing" at his docks, declaring that his buyers could negotiate the best price on the spot. He cautioned his people not to let any boat leave the dock with fish in its hold. As Brickman had predicted, the inbound tonnage was increasing rapidly, with all buyers now deeply in the game, most without an exit plan. Even at the eventual $6,200 per ton price, there was no sense of shortage in the face of the frenzied buying. Even small, one-hoist companies who had never packed herring roe were buying. Everybody was buying. Everyone except Seven Seas. Brickman had ordered his buyers to do everything necessary to slow down their purchases. Fuses would mysteriously blow out, leaving hoist motors stuck in mid-haul. A boat being unloaded effectively blocks the dock for further deliveries. In the heart of the run one of the Seven Seas' loading stations caught fire, burning the hoist and the receiving area before the fire boat could arrive. This only fueled the buying urgency of the others, because it was perceived as an opportunity rather than an omen.

When Barentino heard the news he laughed out loud to his chief financial officer Pete Friscia, who sat across the desk from him. "He's fucked now. This run will be over in ten days. He'll never get repaired in time." Friscia had been running the numbers. "Tom, we're packing 170 tons a day, damn near a million bucks every 24 hours."

"Pete, stop worrying. I was on the phone with Tokyo last night. I'm playing one against the other, as always, and they are trying to 'one-up' each other on the buy."

"But Joe, what about the contracts. Have they signed the deal?"

"Pete, we're going to own the fishery this year, now that Brickman is out of the picture. We can name our price and the Japs will have to pay it!"

What Barentino didn't know was that Brickman had met with the CEO of Daichi Umi before the prior king crab season and promised him that, along with his king crab commitment, Seven Seas would guarantee him "first right of refusal" on the highest quality "early-run" herring roe, and at a price that he guaranteed to be 20 percent under the opening market rate from any other packer. That is if, and only if, Daichi Umi agreed to sign a market order with Seven Seas naming Seven Seas as their exclusive supplier. Because ikura paled in comparison to the massive king crab business, Daichi Umi agreed. The fix was on.

The herring run continued for the next 12 days, with very heavy landings, before tapering off. Though the price had moderated, the average price paid by Barentino was $5,900 per ton, 50 percent higher than the previous season. And at a bank-busting 3,800 tons purchased, he had exhausted his commercial lines of credit, requiring him to pledge his plant and his home as collateral. Only Nissho stepped up when the dust had settled and reluctantly offered a price equivalent to $6,100 per ton. Barentino countered at $6,600. There were initial sales of 100-200 tons at that number before something went very wrong. Daichi Umi and Nissho are rivals, but because there are no anti-trust laws in Japan, the *keiretsu* class[2] of competitors (who often strategize together) had decided that the ikura price was unsustainable.

Brickman chose the lull in the action as an opportunity to confirm one 500-ton sale of "young" ikura to Daichi Umi at $5,800 per ton. That was $100 below the average price paid to the fishermen. The market was stunned, especially Barentino. Brickman kept confirming another 100 tons or so at incrementally lower prices over the next two weeks. By the time the market collapsed, Seven Seas had sold nearly all of its inventory at a profit, and the market was down nearly 30 percent from the Nissho price. The small players were beginning to smell trouble and began dumping their inventories. Because they had little experience in the art of packing ikura (which requires special care and handing), the prices they received were deeply discounted from the benchmark grade. But in a panicked market, the price is the price, and soon the market buzzed with stories of a mysterious buyer from New York paying as little as $3,200 - $3,600 per ton, FOB San Francisco.

---

2 Keiretsu describes a group of companies with interlocking business relationships and shareholdings. The keiretsu has maintained dominance over the Japanese economy for the greater half of the twentieth century.

In the end, the market settled at $4,200 for standard quality, and Seven Seas made a handsome profit buying from distressed sellers, then reselling to Daichi Umi. Barentino had been forced to sell almost 4,000 tons to Nissho, losing more than $1,500 per ton. He even held on to 1,200 tons of stock on the hope that the market would recover. It never did, and in May, Pete Friscia presented a single-sheet profit-and-loss statement to Barentino. The company was down more than $6,000,000 on the herring. Nissho was offering them 60 cents on the dollar on their remaining inventory, creating another $2.4 million loss.

"Joe, there's no way out," Friscia said. "The bank wants their cash now, plus the collateral, if they aren't made whole. They'll give us a few weeks, but honestly it's not going to matter. It's over."

Brickman stopped at his mother's house for an early breakfast before heading to the office. He opened the paper and, below the fold, the left column reported that Joe Barentino had been found by his wife, dead in his garage, seated in his Cadillac with the engine running. No note had been found, and no motive for the suicide had been determined by police. Later, Barentino's estate sued Seven Seas, citing that ". . . anti-trust and RICO law violations had contributed to a predatory attack on Barentino, resulting in the wrongful death of the owner, all at the hands of Seven Seas and its management." Molinari pulled out all the stops, filing an anti-trust counter suit along with a defense that portrayed Barentino as a egomaniacal "nut case" intent on putting all other players out of the business, and creating a virtual monopoly for himself in the ikura trade. The legal strategy worked, with Molinari even exacting legal fees from the Barentino estate.

Ɔ

CHAPTER 13

"OK, I'm beginning to get the message. Expectation setting reduces uncertainty by setting the ground rules on what will happen next, by whom, and when. Make no assumptions, right? And all the while I'm monitoring the relationship part, and I'm paying attention to the personality type of the person I'm dealing with, and then I'm adapting my style accordingly. Again, it's about getting them comfortable and getting the lines of communication open so that they'll answer your questions. To be honest Charles, I hate the thought that I'm changing who I am to accommodate anybody, especially a buyer."

"Listen Jane, it's not about changing yourself. It's about playing a role, which you are subconsciously doing all day, every day, anyway. What are the roles you take on every day? Think about it. Salesperson is only one of the acting jobs you're already performing. You just haven't seen that role in that light. So, here's the epiphany: Now you are going to be aware of it, and that's terrifically liberating. No more guessing about the right thing to say anymore. No more constant self-talk while the other person is talking to you. Just cut it off. No more guessing. From now on, you are going to focus on the other party, on the prospect or the client, and you're going to listen for what their view of reality is, and exactly how their personality type colors their view. Adopt your style to best suit the person you're talking with, and be fully conscious of it — fully aware — fully in the present in those conversations."

After retrieving her bags from the bellman, Jane bids farewell to the fine linens of the Pelham Hotel as Earlsfield drives her to Waterloo Station to catch the Eurostar to Paris.

"Let's see, I depart 18:20 from Waterloo. That gets me to Paris at about quarter of 9, right? I hope Paris is cheaper than London. I don't know how you 'limeys' manage to survive in sales in this country." Then, affecting her best British accent, "Everything's so bloody dear here! All you down at Billingsgate must be poor as church mice."

"Well Dearie," dropping his Queen's English and affecting a Lennon-like Liverpool accent, "We ain't like you colonists over there, still living on the frontier, you know. We've been muddlin' through down in that smelly old market for five centuries, and we'll probably manage another couple-a-more, 'tank-ya' all the same."

Jane's knapping deep in the Rover's glove-leather left seat. Riding back to London, the store tour has revived her sense of humor, and she can't help breaking out in a giggle at his impersonation.

"Actually, this has been a marvelous year. Truly Jane, it takes the biscuit. I'm so looking forward to taking Gracie and the girls to Costa Nova in November. And we've just bought a little bungalow in Falmouth. A bit of a fixer-upper, but a gorgeous location on a hill overlooking the beach."

"Charlie, how are you doing it? Where are you getting this stuff, these ideas, setting up the calls, analyzing the personalities, no samples or brochures? And the whole relationship thing? I mean, I'm a relationship person, right? I know how to warm up to clients."

"Jane, I'm not talking about the traditional 'relationship selling.' That's dead. I'm talking about being deeply relevant while you're on the call. It's about never guessing about the outcome. It's about always finding out. That Kiwi chap David Shepard, he's the 'Just Stop Selling' guy that . . ." Jane interrupts.

"You gotta be kidding! I know David Shepard. I sat with a fellow named David Shepard on the plane. It must be the same guy because he spoke with an Australian accent and we talked about expectations and relationships. I mean, I don't know him, but I rode over on Virgin from Newark with him. He spilled his drink on me!"

"Stone the crows! Now that's a bit scary, isn't it? Jane, David Shepard's work has changed my entire approach to sales. Rather, my whole business philosophy. My life! I did actually speak with him once, very briefly, after a talk he gave at the London School of Economics, which was brilliant, by the way. He's actually a New Zealander, and this 'Guess-Free Selling' thing he teaches is an important business story over here. I'm telling you, you don't know who you were sitting with. His approach is having a profound impact on the way business is conducted around the globe."

For the first time since Jane has known Earlsfield she has elicited a truly emotional reaction from him. She could count on one hand the number of times he has expressed any excitement at all. Typically, he is the epitome of British understatement. Now he's gone all effusive about some business guru.

As he circles the Rover at St. George's onto Waterloo Road, he pounds his fist on the chunky black leather steering wheel.

"Let me tell you, My Dear, it's important stuff. We don't have the time now. The station's just ahead. I'll shoot you an e-mail and we can talk later. But you need to keep that connection with Shepard if you can. It is going to have a very positive impact on your business. What we've talked about so far is just the tip of the iceberg. Remember that. There's a lot more to know."

Nearly up to speed, the train rocks gently as it enters the banked southeasterly curve below Dover before slipping under ground. The increasing pressure plays on her ears and muffles the sound of the rails while closing the world in around the car. Jane feels insulated and softened by the darkness. For a short time she imagines that the train is running under the cliffs and coast and sea and ships and scenes from D-Day and Henry V that played out here hundreds of meters above and decades and centuries before. Now, isolated under all of that, it seems safe and quiet at 180 kilometers per hour, headed to Gaul.

Jane's brain flashes through the previous 24 hours . . . and the coming days. Gus Jambon, Ryan Brickman, the boats, Charlie Earlsfield, Nigel Howard, Mary Smyth, Tom Flowers, David Shepard, and now Brussels by way of Paris. And then to Denver and Carl Christian. What will she say to him? Nothing, probably. Just be there to show solidarity with the family. Why did she ever get involved? But it didn't matter. We each choose our own course. We each make our own decisions. To the extent that we defer our decisions to others, we allow ourselves to blindly accept the dogma that others shovel at us. When we try to live like, or be like, or emulate, or imitate, or compare ourselves to others, we are detracting from our own path. From our own authenticity.

David Shepard! Jane has always felt contemptuous when people spout to her about the latest book, or training, or popular piece of business "bullshit du jour" circulating in the popular business literature. It's all hype. It prays on the tendency of weak people to grab hold of any pundit who holds out the hope of some transformative "snake oil" that will "change your life." She does not want her life changed. In fact, she wants to be more herself. So the less advice and guidance being rained down on her through e-mails and websites and "weekly newsletters" the better. She often deletes every business message that lands in her mailbox. She's the one who knows her business. She understands her philosophy about her business, and about dealing with people, and about selling, and about relationship-building, and it is really thoroughly unnecessary for David Shepard or any other snake-oil-selling Ab-Master Guru of Sales to be peddling her another sales "weight-loss program."

I want more Jane Dreyfus Training, she thinks. I'm tired of tricks and techniques that try to maneuver prospects into the cross hairs. And I'm sick and tired of idiot prospects who think that business with Jane is disposable — just another free consulting gig performed to perfection for procurement folks who are looking for their annual $20,000 bonus by shaving another 0.1 percent off the cost of doing business. I'm just sick and tired of dancing. I want them to dance. That's it. This is the way I want to handle my business going forward. I don't care what Shepard, or Tony Robbins, or the Solution Selling guys, or the Spin selling, or Sandler, or any of these folks say about selling. They're all great. I get it! It just isn't great for me. From now on, they qualify for me. Life is too damn short. Thirteen lives gone in an instant, including Carl's son. What can I possibly say to Carl? I don't even like the guy, and now I need to console him and apologize to him. This just cuts much deeper, that's all. Much deeper than the petty positioning and negotiations. Death trumps it all. The only way to handle death is to walk away from it. With the one lesson that matters: Our time is limited. Don't piss it away living someone else's life. If something doesn't feel right after a few days, make a change. Don't sit around hoping for it to get better. Nothing gets better with time. Deals don't get better, prospects don't, milk doesn't. No more bullshit. Either there's a compelling need and we can figure it out fast, or I'm done. No more of this "Everyone's a prospect. Keep pounding on them until they submit." It's just not working!

The train's pilot comes on and speaks first in English then in French. "We have completed the passage under the channel and soon will be surfacing south of Calais."

The train slows slightly, and there are a few syncopated flashes of bright daylight. She is suddenly ascending through a sea of lavender chrysanthemums flooding out from port and starboard to the hillside horizon of the Sangatte Coast. Jane is dazzled by the scene, her breath taken and freely given for another remarkable glimpse at the beauty and order of it all. She has stood in awe of the great Purams of Vishnu. The atlas Garuda lifting Angkor Watt. The monsoon lightening firing in the skies above Singapore. The naked poor, like saints installed in bas relief on the gates of Zia International. The conspiring mire of sandalwood and sapwood and burning brakes and ringless belching engines gasping from deep below the acid smog that clings to a pre-dawn taxi ride from Calcutta's airport up Hide Street to the Taj Hotel. The crush of children who blocked her climb up Bose Road to visit the nuns of the Sisters of Charity mission, and the "Suddenly Last Summer" escape into the doors of the mission, and the exquisite and quite false righteousness that followed.

Nothing in her life has ever compared to being there, somewhere, far away. Anywhere, where her proximity to what is accustomed, mundane, and ordinary is gone, and in its place, the remarkable experience of being present in an alien place, remote and off-balance and alone. A place where she inevitably encounters a sudden sucker punch of a picture that redefines reality about her human life on earth. A place so fresh and extraordinary that it resets her references for magnificent, malevolent, and the monumental.

CHAPTER 14

"*Chasseures rouges!* Jane, I wear red shoes. Meet me at the Fontaine Moliere. We will eat. It's OK with you?" The phone goes dead.

Melina Bunge is the daughter of Francois Bunge, current patriarch of a dynasty of Jewish agents and traders who have negotiated European food agreements for generations through war, revolution, and unification from their offices at 20 Rue Gudin. Bunge had contacted Jane about Bunge acting as the Seven Seas broker for king crab and Alaska salmon in the European Union. But where the hell is Moliere Fountain?

Jane is looking forward to the talk because Bunge is known for having an aggressive style, which fits Jane perfectly. Jane is easily bored with business conversations that don't go anywhere. She wants ideas and value from her conversations, one way or the other, and she doesn't abide indecision or intellectual dullness when it comes to business talk. This means that her resolve to be politically correct could weaken in the context of business small talk, and this has proven a liability at times. People often see her as abrupt and undiplomatic, which for years she's worn as a badge of honor. She is learning, however, that it could also be a liability. She has been working on becoming more externally focused during her conversations. Particularly personal ones.

She is also slowly becoming aware that to get what she wants from others, it is often more productive to understand what they are looking to accomplish first. She has (reluctantly) become aware that her inwardly focused approach, regardless of how intelligent, skilled, and knowledgeable, is limiting. And in business, the consequences of not having an outward focus seems to be more and more negative as she moves into higher levels of prospect management and authority.

Jane is coming to realize more and more that she needs to adapt her communications to the important fact that, in business, it is always and forever about the prospect. They don't give a damn about Jane, or the company she represents.

She remembers that WIIFM — "my favorite radio station" — is one of many jabs that Brickman takes at her when he feels she's becoming self-deluded or a little off track. "When you're feeling too good about a prospect meeting, or when a negotiation has gotten tough and you are thinking about a concession, just remember 'What's in it for me?'"

Prospects are no different, whether or not they are focused on it during a sales call. Either during the conversation or after, they will be evaluating the meeting in terms of "What, exactly, is in it for me," and if you haven't managed to jolt them — drive home the payoff before you finish — the deal will be dead before the door closes behind you. You'll be written off as inconsequential, which kills you in the mind of the buyer for life. Irrelevance is a terminal condition.

But how to make it happen? Especially these days when it seems that prospects are even better informed than Jane is on the current details of the business, the options, and, hell, even the prices! How can you get on top of that?

At the same time, she is becoming more and more suspect of the whole "relationship selling" methodology. She has always been suspicious of people who want to talk about golf before they talk about business. But today, focusing any time on the pictures of the rafting trip on the office wall, or where to go for lunch, before learning anything about the prospect's business issues or aspirations, seems like a supreme farce. Prospects need funds, not friends. Every minute I spend that isn't lasered in on the business is a minute wasted. Period. But what's the alternative? What's the answer to dealing with prospects who are supremely informed and neither care nor have the time to even learn your name. Just what is the answer?

The small green triangle formed by Moliere and Richelieu streets is crowded, and though she is 15 minutes early, Jane begins scanning the feet of the people huddled by the fountain. She's searching for the red shoes. She has often thought shoes to be the most telling indicator of the character and personality of a person, and she is captivated by the mini-Parisian biography of the group assembled by the fountain.

"I love it with Americans. They are on time, always. It is perfect!" From just behind and above Jane's right ear comes a low Piafian growl of a voice. She turns on her heels, catching a flash of the red shoes, then tilts her head back to greet a charming Duchenne smile gazing at her. A shock of fresh orange-red hair cascades down the woman's shoulders and over her brilliant emerald-green waist coat and skirt. Melina Bunge's sinewy, athletic frame stands two inches above Jane's 5-foot-7, and Jane recoils momentarily from the imposition.

"Mon Dieu, but you are pretty for a fish-cutting girl! Let me see your hands. I want the proof!"

Jane has been looking forward to the meeting with Bunge for yet another reason: This is one of the rare occasions when she will be the buyer, not the seller. Bunge had initiated the contact with her through Brickman when she was inquiring about the Seven Seas sales brokerage opportunity for the EU market. Naturally, Jane had anticipated that Bunge would attempt to romance Seven Seas at this meeting, relating the history of the F. Bunge company and its clients, along with her own significant industry experience. Basically, a French version of the standard "salesy," unctuousness that she found at best, entertaining, and at worst, contemptuous, from sales people in any industry.

But it's already clear that this conversation will be different. Bunge had caught her off guard with the directness of her greeting, both inquisitive and highly relevant, and essentially so personal that Jane could not resist the compliment implied by it. She felt compelled to respond honestly, though self-consciously, and, without so much as a formal greeting, her reply stumbled out. Her well-laid plans on how she would control the conversation — and how she intended to set the stage for negotiations to maximize the advantage for herself and Seven Seas — were now scrambled.

"Why yes. Well, ummm, you can see my hands are not pretty. Too many scars. I'm proud of them, though, but too many knives."

Jane is self-conscious, but strangely encouraged that her conversation has started out on such an unpretentious footing. None the less, she attempts to gain some conversational control, and awkwardly affects a more commanding tone of voice.

"Melina, it is a pleasure to meet you. Tell me, is there a place to sit nearby? I have some questions to ask about your message to Ryan."

Bunge guides her across the street, around the circle, and up Richelieu.

"Oustaou is my friend's café here. *Fantastique*. His father was the chef for the Reagans. In fact, he had a restaurant in California. Perhaps you know Rene Vermond."

They are seated by the window. The breeze outside stirs a newspaper that lifts and drifts across their view. Jane catches one word visible in the headline, *"Tuer."*

Bunge's flawless skin clings tightly to her skull, wrapping each muscle and bone of her face with the iconic allure of Echaillon marble. This compared to Jane's Schuylkill River clay completion. Her sea-green her eyes have a relaxed, but predatorial, presence and are locked on Jane with an elevating effect. Her posture and casual elegance is striking. Her beauty is, in a word, purposeful. Her smile is full-face and warm, with each muscle engaged right down to her lips, which rest slightly opened and lopsided. But her smile is guarded by just the hint of a scowl that seems could signal a kiss or a kill with the mildest modification.

"Jane, how is your time today? I actually have 90 minutes myself. Is that good with you? We will eat and then maybe we go to my office for a coffee. It's on Rue de Conde, near the palace." Her cell phone rings. "I'm sorry, my phone is interrupting us too often, so I will close it before we start."

Jane nods in agreement.

"Also, though I speak it poorly, I understand English very well. My use is not always best, so please ask me if you don't understand something I've said. Jane, first to say thank you from me and my company for coming to meet. I've read about your wonderful Seven Seas company, on the web, and, of course, we know the re-pu-ta-see-on of Seven Seas. Maybe you have heard something of F. Bunge also? Of course, you have many options for brokers for your products in the EU. But you have taken my invitation to meet with us. I am curious: Why us? Why F. Bunge? Why did you and Monsieur Brickman expect that this would be a good meeting for you?"

Bunge's steady, nearly monotone, voice reveals little, if any, anticipation or anxiety over any particular outcome of their conversation. It occurs to Jane that the voice is professional, warm, and engaging, but not at all enthralled. She certainly appears interested, but not forward leaning. A bit like a doctor who you were going to visit for the first time for a diagnosis.

"It just so happened that I was traveling through the city on my way to a conference tomorrow. I had asked my assistant, Doug, to arrange a visit with you, if possible. I really don't know much about your firm, but you had reached out to us when we went looking for a broker for the EU market."

Jane has actually known of F. Bunge for years. The company has a reputation as an important player in the EU market, but they have always had their own particular style of doing business. They are exclusive agents, meaning they will only represent one manufacturer in a given vertical, and they're known for rejecting more business than they take on. One of Jane's early mentors, Hugh Lavern, once told her that F.Bunge was simply the best in the business when it came to EU representation. Further, part of their appeal was their very astute aligning of their manufacturers and buyers, because they take the time to qualify both before committing to delivering a deal. When Melina Bunge sent Brickman an e-mail offering to discuss an exclusive arrangement, both he and Jane were pleased with the prospect that they would have a top-performing partner selling for them in Europe.

Bunge leans across the table with a smile and embracing laughter while reaching out and touching Jane's hand. "Dear Jane, I'm sorry. First I should say 'Welcome to Paris,' of course. It is wonderful that you would arrange to meet with me. Tell me if there is anything I can do for you while you are here."

Then, raising her head Bunge sits back in the chair, crosses her legs, and unbuttons her waist coat. Though she does not appear particularly fashionable, Jane can see by the wool, the weave, and fine thread count of her linen blouse, that she has an appreciation for refined quality. She wears very little jewelry, except for modest diamond-stud earrings. On her left wrist is an Iron Woman watch. On her right, a braided hobble-knot bracelet. Through her spare makeup radiates a beauty of strength and dispassionate confidence. In a word, she is distinguished, and there seems no hint of distraction in her manor, in her visage, or in the directness of her words.

"Tell me Jane, why is this meeting important to you? What is it that caused you to begin thinking about representation in the EU, or about F. Bunge?"

Jane is reluctant to talk about the real reason that motivated her inquiry for an EU agent. Just six months prior, Seven Seas had taken a $350,000 hit at the hands of EU customs in Le Havre when two ocean containers of shrimp from Thailand were embargoed. One was destroyed by the health authorities, and the other was held for reconditioning under suspicions that certain contents were tainted with chloramphenicol[1]. The restricted contaminant recently had been outlawed for use in aquaculture food supplies. Exporters had scrambled to become compliant with the new regulations, because, thanks to the latest high-performance liquid-chromatography technology, even

---

1   A broad-spectrum antibiotic that is both cheap and easy to manufacture. It is frequently a drug of choice in the Third World. Due to resistance and safety concerns, it is rarely used as a first-line agent for infections in developed nations.

nano-metric levels can be detected. Seven Seas had always pursued the strategy of selling directly to major end-users, therefore garnering all of the profit. That occasionally lead to a bit of deliberation when it came to regulatory matters. This was Jane's painful, expensive, and uninsured lesson learned, and now is the time for her to face the facts and look for help.

"Meli, we're just looking at expanding our business. We have greater capacity to produce, particularly in the king crab line, and we want to look further into the EU market as an option. And some recent developments are encouraging us to do just that."

Bunge speaks firmly, "Well, maybe, as we say, 'the banana is still green' on this project. Perhaps there is some additional time to consider the options. We're not a complement for all companies, I must tell you. Depending on what you are looking for as an outcome, I am not sure that we can fit together. What are these recent developments that you speak of?"

"Well, there's the currency. Japan has grown to dominate the export side, and we're looking to spread our risk. We also anticipate increased production. And Europe can be challenging to trade in. I mean the regulations and the multiple markets, etc., so we …"

"Challenges? What challenges do you see?"

"Melina, let me ask you first about what you are charging for your services. This will have a lot to do with the rest of our conversation."

Smiling, Bunge nods her head, and casts her eyes to the street beyond. The sun is shooting a dazzling shaft across the Rue Richelieu, and the autumn breeze tosses small cyclones of leaves at Jardin Palais Royal, one block to the east.

As Bunge pauses, Jane becomes uncomfortable. At the same time, Bunge wonders if Jane believes her story? Is she offended by the question? Why does she seem to want to control this conversation? After all, I am the customer. I should be in charge here, Bunge reasons.

"Jane, I will answer your question. But first, if you don't mind, I will tell you that there are many terrific brokers in Europe who can represent you well. When you are in Brussels you will find many that I am sure will be very excited to talk with you. And I will say that F. Bunge does not have the lowest rates of commission. We are considered by some to have high rates. I really don't know. The overall cost of the business is another question. I must ask you, is cost the reason for your decision? If so, that would be a *'feu rouge'*[2] I think, because we are not the, uh, cheapest."

Jane is becoming visibly irritated. Her chair has become uncomfortable. She diverts her eyes from side to side, to avoid looking directly at Bunge. The conversation has turned from an interview of a candidate to Jane being interviewed by the broker. And she doesn't like it. Is it these French? She has never liked the French.

2 red light

"We'll," Jane says, "I suppose that we have much work to do on this before we make a decision. Tell me about your firm — your size and your current principals and customers."

"Actually we are very small. May I ask, does this disqualify us? Because we are only 11, including our administration?"

The conversation continues with Jane becoming increasingly emotional over her lack of control of the process, and Bunge's unvarnished questions about the auguries of her business, all the time seeming to push back, as if she is not even interested in Seven Seas' business. If she couldn't get F. Bunge, who will she talk with? Who can she trust to handle her current mess and help her avoid any further EU disasters? Bunge shifts her chair from a quarter-way around the circular, amber-granite café table.

"Jane, forgive me for being so forward. But typically, when a principal approaches us, there is a specific reason. Something has happened to cause them great worry, risk, uncertainty, or opportunity in their business. It is never without an important reason. This is generally the only reason people make such an important decision. So my questions are to understand the reality of your situation, because, in business, it can be hard to come to the truth without knowing those reasons. Can we come back to the challenges you referred to before? How difficult are they? Are they really of any importance to the overall success of your company? If you are just smelling the flowers, you are not qualified for F. Bunge. Do you understand? It never works out."

With a little more prodding by Bunge, Jane opens up with the entire story of her issues with EU embargo, and the current fiasco that could exceed a million dollars, after logistical and legal fees. Even with two attorneys and their customs broker, the problem is only getting worse.

"Melina, this is a disaster, truly, and with career implications. I need to solve this fast before matters get worse." Jane punctuates her sentence with a glance down at the empty cup in her left hand, while brushing her hair back from her forehead with the heel of her thumb. Bunge calls for another coffee.

"You are jet lagged, and little tired from traveling. Again, I don't know if F. Bunge can help you in this situation. It is complex. But if you want to, we can walk over to my office and talk about some details of an arrangement, and what it would look like, and I will answer your questions about our rates."

Jane is relieved as they depart the café and begin walking east on Moliere. Bunge provides a brief referential description of their location in the city to key points of interest as she begins asking questions about Jane's prior visits to France. Her line of questioning is remarkably refreshing, compared to the typical boring light conversation that Jane generally avoids. Bunge is almost childlike in the total lack of pretense or presumption in her questions: "Is the business in king crab very profitable? What are your responsibilities in the export business? Do they pay you very much money to do the work you do? What is the expected outcome of the meetings with F. Bunge? What would be the ideal outcome for Mr. Brickman if there was a mutual decision to work together?"

❧

CHAPTER 15

Following his introduction, David Shepard steps to the lectern and switches off the microphone. "I'm a loud, hyperactive sales guy who can't stand behind podiums anyway, so we won't need this." There's an audible chuckle throughout the audience.

It is the second session on a crystal-clear alpine morning. The sun's rays have just now climbed free of the Bernese Alps, and begin streaming through the eastern leaded-glass windows that encircle the ancient domed ceiling of the amphitheater of the Swiss College of Surgeons, like the clearstory of a cathedral. For the earlier first session, the group had heard a highly technical lecture on the latest techniques in "Phased Electromagnetic Radiation for the Non-invasive Destruction of Tumors." They had left the room for a coffee break and the selection of local pastries and cheeses of Old Bern. Now they had returned for Shepard's session.

His program is titled: "On reducing malpractice risk through specific patient investigation methodologies." An international medical malpractice insurance firm had approached Shepard, after he had trained the company's sales staff, about the application of his methodologies by medical doctors to help reduce the number and severity of malpractice claims. They had offered to sponsor his presentation at this conference of its high-incidence policy holders, surgical oncologists. There is growing evidence of a connection between the doctor-patient relationship and post-surgical issues. Two recent studies suggest that pre-op polling of patients who score physicians low on indicators for "trust, empathy and authenticity" served well as a predictor for the likelihood of malpractice claims. Further, and even more remarkably, the results seem to suggest that the likelihood of a claim filing is somewhat independent of the actual medical outcome of procedures. There is increasing evidence that a physician's inability to convey a sense of genuine human concern about patients and their families resulted in a perception of uncertainty. And that, in turn, can translate into an elevated the risk of a malpractice claim, even in the absence of obvious harm. A second study reveals the interesting correlation that, in spite of records of actual negative outcomes from surgery, patients who trusted their physicians were often reluctant to take legal action against them, even though there was ample justification do so. Shepard's goal, today, is to conduct a workshop that instills in the doctors there some of the benefits of his "guess-free" investigation process to give them some skills to help them better deal with the inherent fear and uncertainty that their patients experience when facing cancer.

Shepard clears his throat and begins speaking, as a picture of a modest yellow chapel nestled in a grove of jujube trees fills the large screen above his head.

"I had the occasion to visit this Portuguese church near Madras on St. Thomas Mount, about 20 kilometers south of the city. This is where it is alleged that the Apostle was martyred by a local potentate named Misdeus after Thomas had converted the man's

wife and son to Christianity. Legend has it that it wasn't Thomas'
religion or righteousness or inspired genius that finally drove the
king to have him speared to death on top of a granite hill from
which spot ever since a cold, clear spring has flowed from an
otherwise arid landscape. No, Thomas was killed by the king,
so it is said, because Thomas was a doubter. He was apparently
a master at creating uncertainty." Then, leaning forward toward
the audience, "Not the type of person you'd want assisting you in
surgery, am I right?" Again an audible chuckle from the surgeons.
"It is said that he often conveyed doubt to his followers through
his remoteness and his tendency to remain isolated and apart from
them. His poor communications skills engendered a disturbing
sense of dread in their minds about their new faith, at precisely
the time when they needed the most encouragement. Suffice to say,
they were in an emotionally vulnerable condition, especially in
first-century India. Not unlike recently diagnosed cancer patients
today. Thomas was terrifically talented at his craft, but he was
also terrifically bad at developing trusting relationships with other
people. And for it, old King Misdeus, whose own wife was a
recent convert, decided to have him killed."

"Now, you are all brilliant surgeons, I get that. Your talents,
your experience, and your knowledge place you at the top of the
medical profession, and much more relative than us mere mortals."

Laughter erupts as Shepard continues, "In fact, with the current
web-based systems of ranking physicians, the public can find out
just how brilliant you really are. But curiously, when it comes
to malpractice, the rate of claims filed against a given physician
has little to do with his or her professional peer-ranking scores
for expertise. What it does relate to are the so-called 'patient

empowerment scores.' These scores, in general, predict how physicians are ranked by patients on trustworthiness and competence. Patients are asked specific questions about the confidence and trust they have in their doctors. And patients increasingly have the power to rank and to choose their doctors, based on those rankings. Like it or not, this measurement of patient trust is becoming more and more critical to the ability of you to be successful at sustaining and building your private practice."

Another audible murmur rolls through the crowd then quickly drops away.

"Your work is becoming commoditized, and market and legislative pressures will continue to reduce medical care and medical procedures to the lowest common denominator. To prosper, you need to build a practice based increasingly on private (non-insurance) patients, and these people tend to be the wealthiest and most highly educated 2.5 percent of the population. They're the ones who are effectively self-insured for health risk, and they seldom hesitate to pay out of their own pockets for procedures, if they find that the insurance or regulatory environment gives them no, or only a limited, choice of least-cost alternatives. This patient population not only has the money to make elective medical choices, but they are educated in finding physicians, especially through digital means, who have been highly ranked by previous patients, based on the outcome of dealing with them. I am connecting the dots here between the future patient populations who can pay you, and the necessity to develop specific processes for dealing with patients in a way that gives them confidence, trust, and faith in your medical abilities, and in you personally.

I am talking here about "worthy intent." I am talking about learning to create a conversation with each of your patients that consistently conveys your intention that their — your patients' — best outcome is at the core of your patient-doctor relationship."

Shepard often uses his "Doctor's Story" when training sales teams in the principles of the "Guess-Free Sales" method. The tool conveys the efficiency a doctor brings to investigating the issues, and getting the patient emotionally engaged in the possible outcomes. There is irony in the fact that he is now presenting the same material to doctors themselves. The concept is based on the notion that doctors are, in effect, the world's best sales people, because they are able to motivate patients to urgent, unconditional action with the simple inference of a life-threatening medical condition. The notion that doctors never have to sell themselves is central to his lesson. An physician need only to gaze in a concerned way at an x-ray, and with simple "Hmmmm" make patients ready to forfeit house and home if the doctor can tell how to save themselves.

"But what can be done in the diagnosis process — what we typically call 'investigation management' — to mitigate the likelihood of an unhappy, distrustful, and reactionary patient? Well, the most effective way to develop a trusting relationship with any individual is to create a sense of shared fate. Ask the kind of reality-testing questions that allow them to discover the truth of their own condition in the context of what we as a team (patient, physician, surgical staff) are going to do to try to fix it. There are eight fundamental Reality-Testing Questions." He moves to his next slide.

Clarification	"Can you elaborate? …illustrate? …give examples?"
Accuracy	"Is this true or false? How can we verify this?"
Precision	"Can you be more specific? Can you give more detail? Can you be more exact?"
Depth	"Why is this so difficult? What are the complexities?"
Relevance	"How does this relate? How does this help us with the issue?"
Logicalness	"Does this make sense? Does it follow from the evidence?"
Significance	"Is this important? What is most important? Is this the most important?"

"These are familiar to you from the diagnostic process. The key here is to broaden the scope of use and provide your patients with the opportunity to voice to you the root of their concerns. You do not want the patient to make the assumption that you understand it all because you have encountered similar cases time and time again. The key is that each case is unique in the mind of the patient. There is a source of great uncertainty on their part, and this is exactly what we are trying to mitigate."

"There are six basic strategies for using these RTQs, with the objective of eliminating uncertainty about you in the mind of your patient, while developing a stronger, more confident and trusting relationship."

"The first strategy: Ask the patient for help. Avoid the tendency to present canned solutions to a patient's problems. Remain inconclusive with them about your prognosis, if you have formulated any, and instead, focus on what the patient is feeling and thinking. 'Help me to understand what you are experiencing, the level of pain, and the limitations this condition is placing on your life.'"

Number two, allow your patient to express why they would not want to proceed with the surgery. What conditions, or other individuals, might influence their decisions about moving forward?"

Number three, from the outset, be realistic. Don't fear being too honest about the risks inherent in a procedure, or the probability of successful outcomes. Claims that 'it will all work out OK' are often viewed with skepticism, and can result in an elevated sense of uncertainty and mistrust of you. Even if you are 100 percent confident in the outcome of the procedure, always express a realistic view."

Next, softening and cushioning statements should be used whenever discussing issues as sensitive as surgery. Assertions made about success rates and 'cones of probability' should always be couched in words that are sensitive to the sensibilities of the person receiving them. 'That's a good question. I'm glad you asked that. That's an important point.' These are all softening phrases."

Number five, reversing a patient's question often leads to the real motive behind the question, or a concern that could come up later and cause trouble. If a patient asks you one question, and you suspect that something else is on their mind, send the question back to them. For example, a prostate cancer patient who is avoiding an agreement to have surgery may be principally concerned with post-op virility issues, but he may not be direct in questioning you about it."

And number six, if your patient is minimizing the problem, it is a form of denial that you probably shouldn't fight, or they will just become more entrenched. It's best is to minimize the problem along with them, and then inform them about the most probable consequences of inaction."

"It is always our intention to allow the reality of the diagnosis to sink in to the mind of the patient, rather than us trying to force it in. That latter techniques will only result in mistrust and further uncertainty at a time when the patient is already very vulnerable. It is key when you are investigating the condition of a patient that you never deny the crucial importance of the patient's own powers of perception about the outcome of the surgery, regardless of the actual physiological results of the procedure. It is well established that this perception is founded on a patient's relationship with their physician to the extent that the doctor has succeeded in establishing a sense of trust. Further, there is a methodology for establishing that trust through the deliberate strategy of creating a sense of shared fate between the doctor and patient. These strategies can be studied and integrated into your daily process of patient evaluation and communication. It follows that the implementation of these strategies can be correlated to improvements in the level of confidence and a reduction in the probability that any given procedure will result in a claim for malpractice, regardless of the actual outcome."

There is stunned silence as the doctors soak in Shepard's message: That from a practical perspective, their scientific expertise can take them only so far toward success in their fields. And, indeed, the number of malpractice actions against them is a cogent measure of that success, and an important influence on their performance and their professional satisfaction.

In his brief address Shepard highlighted an important "dark cloud" hanging over all physicians, particularly surgeons, from the moment they swear the Hippocratic Oath until the day they retire. Shepard brought the idea to the surface, and proposed an initiative to mitigate its effects. Every doctor knows about the true cost spurious malpractice claims. All of them know about unscrupulous lawyers who do post-surgical solicitations of patients whose names had been acquired "under the table" from hospital staff. Now there is something they themselves can do to systematically reduce the likelihood of legal action. It fundamentally comes down to the patient-doctor relationship.

A round of applause rises to the dome as Shepard walks off the stage. As usual, he had started sharply on time and ended within two minutes of his mark. Since he typically works with sales teams, he had had special concerns about the kind of reception he would receive from this group. But now, as one after another approaches the dais with copies of his book, he has the sense that he got it right, again. His own criteria for any successful talk include the prevailing relevance of the subject matter, and whether the speaker manages to create a deep emotional connection with the audience. Today, their rapt attention during his presentation confirmed the relevance of his content. But emotional engagement is required to motivate attendees to step up, and judging by the number of the surgeons lining up to talk, he felt secure that he'd accomplished the mission.

Every once in a while he allows himself to consider that it was just possible that the Guess-Free Sales methodology has broader application than simply in the sales context. He often wonders if there is something about the message of "turning the telescope around," and taking the spotlight off you, that can reduce the friction and increase the speed of outcomes in other areas of human endeavor.

ɕ

CHAPTER 16

Lauren Hapides loves Ryan Brickman. To her mind, he personifies the ideal man. Strong, independent, tough. Even notorious. Oh yeah, and a passionate, bone-crusher of a lover. But she also hates him for everything he isn't. He is good, but not loyal. He is great fun, but seldom serious. He makes no promises, and never keeps any either. She can never turn him down, and he never calls her back. It is fire and ice, and she steams over it each time they are together.

"Ryan, I've got three boats lined up who'll sell out for the right price. They all have quota, crews, and are certified. But you're not the only buyer in the market right now, so I don't expect much leeway, if any, on price."

She pauses for a moment, then turns her eyes away from the presentation book and locks them on Brickman's. He cracks the same trademark lop-sided smile that shattered her resistance the very first time they met. No, no. Today it just makes her angry.

"Sorry for asking this, Ryan. We've done a lot of business together, and I've never questioned your thinking. But this time it's different. Frankly, I don't understand your hurry to replace those boats.

You'll get paid soon on the insurance claim, and the continuity rider covers Seven Seas for the down time. Why not find a couple of independents to come over to the Seven Seas side, wait for the claim check, then go boat shopping when the quota's full? If you buy a boat here in mid-season, you'll be paying the top of the market, especially with everyone thinking that you've shorted the crab market. It's like trying to buy a shovel in the middle of a snow storm."

He shamelessly scans her body with the same rakish gaze that she has come to expect. Though he is disciplined about internal relationships, when it comes to working with women outside of the company, Brickman was up front and unrestrained about what interested him most. She swore that each time he greeted her he was replaying the last time they'd slept together. And here it is again. But now it's just pissing her off.

Hapides' cool demeanor isn't lost on him. Not a word mentioned about the wreck. Not even a comment about the loss of life, or of Anacortes Boat Works' role in the construction of the boats. ABW had spent more than a year building the two boats, and there had to be a least a sentimental link to the fact that the pair had taken 13 men down on their maiden trips.

Lauren Hapides is vice president of sales for Anacortes Boat Works. ABW has built and brokered high-seas fishing craft in the Pacific Northwest since the days when the schooner ships rounded Tierra del Fuego loaded with Alaskan iced halibut and canned salmon bound for Boston and New York.

She is an engineer by education, and has prepared a technical presentation for Brickman and Art Lesterman (head of production at Seven Seas) in the offices of Mike Molinari, Seven Seas' attorney, in Seattle. Akna Chernoff, Brickman's partner, is on the conference telephone line from Homer. She knows that Brickman is the money guy, and the only one who can give the final "Yes" to ink the deal. But she also understands that Lesterman's operations team will be responsible for the heavy lifting of getting the deal delivered and paid. The lawyer's job is to "check all the boxes" to be sure that the specifications and conditions on the deal have been met. "Just checking that the ink in the pen is the right color blue," as Molinari put it.

What she didn't understand was the presence of Chernoff on the speakerphone. He has hardly said a word so far, and at the start of the call, when she made the rounds asking what each of them wanted to hear about, he'd just grunted and said, "What's your commission?"

Brickman raises his right hand and gestures out the window across Puget Sound to the Northwest. (Molinari can't help but notice the striking similarity of his gesture to another bearded image to the ceiling of the Sistine Chapel.)

"There are over a hundred boats fishing the Bering Sea right now, loaded with crab, and they're all going to be steaming at full throttle on a fast clock to empty their live tanks and get back out to sea before the crab dies or some other boat beats them to some hot grounds. Each time they head out I'm rolling the dice on whether or not they'll come back to a Seven Seas hoist. I want to make damn sure that at least two of those boats are coming back to me."

"OK Ryan, I've got it." Hapides pauses. "Let's say that one or more of these boats is a buy for Seven Seas. And, by the way, I'm not presuming anything. I'm just suggesting that it could happen if the numbers all work out. I've always sold you new boats, so this deal will be different from our business in the past because we'll be selling a fully operational boat that's already on the water, fishing. Help me understand what's important to you in closing a deal like this? What do you see as the steps for getting a deal signed at this time?"

Brickman hands off her question to Lesterman, then, in turn, to Molinari, to fill in the details of approving the purchase and getting the boats operational as soon as possible. Even though the others provided Hapides with guidance, she knows that Brickman is the ultimate decision maker, and that neither of the other two guys have the authority to say "Yes" to spending money of this size. Each of them does have the power to say "No" however, and she needs to make sure that their concerns are acknowledged and addressed satisfactorily, or they could derail the whole thing.

Brickman is known as a manager who doesn't get in the way of his people when it comes to doing their work or making decisions. Though he is quick to get problems out on the table, and can be brutal about digging through the guts of an issue to get to the truth. His management philosophy boils down to one sentence, often repeated when any conflict arises at Seven Seas: "What can blow us up will weld us together." It's a motto that encourages every employee to have his say about any gripe, as long as it is about getting the work done in the safest, fastest, and most efficient way possible.

The presentation over, Brickman gives Hapides a squeeze, and as she leaves the room, he watches a 747 banking east over the sound with massive Mount Rainier blue and brooding in the background to the southeast. He begins speaking, to no one in particular.

"If I can just find $7 million in cash, we can buy two boats with quota, and hedge the bookings to Hoffman. Without the boats we won't make the distro plan and the Hoffman contract will fail."

He gazes down at a circular plaza, 15 floors below, formed by concentric rings of red herringbone brick and a central fountain. Like Place de la Concorde, he thinks. "Blood-sucking attorneys" he says, while running the arithmetic of getting the boats operational, and the legal fees to get it all done.

He abruptly turns his back to the window, "What about the insurance payment? When will we have the it?"

Molinari jumps in. "Ryan, here's the reality. The carrier will look to verify the claim, which could take 60 to 90 days. Meanwhile, there is no business continuity endorsement in the policy, so until they pay the claim, we're on the hook for the payments to the bank for the boat loan, which is collateralized by the capital construction fund. Plus, since you have no working company vessels or quota, there's no revenue from the fishing company. On those grounds, the bank could conceivably call the loan."

From the moment he received news of the sinkings, Brickman has been considering the problem of restoring Seven Seas' fishing capacity before the quota runs out and the season is over. Failure means they are hostage to the Russian crab supplies to fulfill obligations to Hoffman and the other retailers. A sobering prospect. indeed. The Russians enjoy significant king crab production within their territorial waters. But their logistics and processing capability is medieval and corrupt. Brickman needs the Russians because they are an important hedge for supplying his annual contracts with retailers. The Russian grade is adequate for retail, but it can't compare with the Alaska A-grade, and that production mainly goes to Japan. The challenge with Russian crab is that it requires extensive regrading, butchering, and repackaging, before it can be sent to market in the U.S. and Europe. Seven Seas has found that high-quality workmanship and low labor costs in Vietnam provide the best location for the repack operation. And because the Saigon government has designated portions of the port as a free-trade zone, Seven Seas can move the Russian product in and out of the country, duty free, and with little documentation or government surveillance. The only problem is the Russian bureaucrats who are in charge of the Federation's king crab co-op. With control over the quota, production, and processing, they run the co-op like their personal ATM, and they're ruthless about assuring that it keeps spitting out as much cash as possible.

There is no doubt that word has already reached Vladivostok that Seven Seas has lost one third of its crab-landing capacity, and Brickman knows that "Stalin" (his nickname for Arkady Gasparov, Russia's king crab czar) will soon begin tightening the screws on the invoice price, even though contractually the price is fixed by a weekly indexed formula. It is a constant source of frustration for Brickman that non-G7 contracts are often as thin as the paper they were written on, and (as a practical matter) effectively unenforceable in the event market conditions change and the advantage shifts to the supplier side. With the massive dollars at stake, there will be little room for finesse once Gasparov reneges on the indexed pricing agreement due to "extraordinary market conditions." Brickman's only "best alternative to a negotiated agreement" will be to threaten to dump the contracts with the Russians if the negotiations become too thorny. Since there are always consequences when deals sour with the Russians, "brinksmanship" is to be avoided at all costs.

Brickman has met Gasparov on a number of occasions to discuss crab deals, and he learned quickly that they share a common philosophy about business, that is, an abiding belief in what Brickman refers to as "entrepreneurial immortality."

Only a few opponents who Brickman has ever encountered display his characteristic fearlessness in negotiations — a heart-pounding addiction to an at-the-edge, nose-to-nose, survival-of-the-fittest style. He attributes it to Gasparov's career as a "hunter-killer" commander in the Russian submarine fleet, which sailed from Vladivostok. Gasparov specialized in the Eastern Pacific Ocean, and had plied the Bering Sea for nearly a decade, snapping the pot-lines and blowing ballast tanks under terrified American king crabbers, just for the sport of it. But his tenure on the subs was abruptly cut short by "Gorby's" glasnost, perestroika, and the end of the cold war. Nuclear ballistic-missile submarines and their captains became a luxury in the new era of Russian *kapitalism.* The government wisely chose to redeploy their military assets toward winning the globalized business war. Gasparov landed a coveted Director job with a state corporation — the Russia Research Institute of Marine Fisheries and Oceanography — where he is responsible for the management of Russia's king crab fishery and the lucrative leadership of the crab marketing board.

To Brickman, Gasparov has just the right temperature of ice water in his veins. Brickman admires anyone with the guts to go "balls-out" when the going gets tough, and that goes for allies and opponents alike. Experience has taught Brickman the absolute futility of fear as a basis for business decisions. His belief is based, not on any particular courageousness, but instead on the realization that fear provides no practical advantage to the achievement of his goals. In fact, fear often impeded the critical mental processes of evaluating business issues and opportunities objectively and dispassionately — what he called "the facts and numbers." Though Brickman has a reputation as a "gut-instinct" manager, few people understand that his legendary decisiveness has been fine-tuned through years of mental discipline that have focused his analytical skills to deadly accuracy on issues and opportunities most critical to the success of the business at any place and any time. He also has an uncanny ability to disregard peripheral distractions. He has learned that issues that emerge in an emotional context are always the most deceptively wasteful.

Fear is the worst of them. He believes fear and uncertainty are the main destroyers of business, and even of human achievement. He long ago challenged himself to rid his thinking of those two poisons — permanently. Defeating uncertainty is as simple as rejecting all assumptions, and, whenever possible, learning the truth for himself.

He called it "immortality," for the powerful sense of well-being and freedom that comes from having complete confidence in his decisions and actions. Regardless of what conditions are imposed on him, his predetermined outcomes will prevail as long as he always presses forward toward what he calls the "money truth." No assumptions, no guessing. His outcomes always meet or exceed what he has envisioned, because he is never surprised. His rule of asking reality-testing questions until the facts and factors become clear to him means there's no chance of failed outcomes. Achievement is assured through vigilance and optimal adaptation of his vision to the evolution of the current truth in any dynamic business situation. He never allows himself to become ossified in a particular plan or strategy. The only possible goal of the business is the continuous creation of the commercial world as he sees fit to have it unfold. It is not serving others, nor bending to someone else's vision of reality. That is slavery. The greatest internal battle is to keep the presence of mind that the planets are spinning at the tip of his finger. And to remain always vigilant, always the worthy steward of this deep responsibility to himself.

"Pressing on" means excitement and achievement. That's real life. Hesitation to act, useless deliberation, and rigidity — even when the path ahead is clear — always leads to failure. To Brickman, the terror, the horror, the dark heart of man is inaction. "In business, simply standing still, kills."

Gasparov is different. He has signaled from the outset of their relationship that, with him, negotiating is about deception and submission, a "take no prisoners" blood sport that Brickman finds entertaining. In fact, he prefers that approach to the alternative — hours of useless BS. But Gasparov is essentially a thug — a criminal — who is devoid of honor and conscience. Brickman has learned to feign slowness and confusion when negotiating with him because his statements could range from merely misleading to blatantly false. He might act to delay, disrupt, or derail talks, just when it appeared a deal is eminent, and he did so simply to enrage his opponent. The Hotel La Brusca fiasco was one of his best.

Back in 2001, Brickman had agreed to meet Gasparov at the Hotel La Brusa, on Guantanamo Bay, to finalize and celebrate their crab agreement. Brickman and Chernoff sweated for six hours in the decrepit, 1950s-era bar, sipping warm rum and Coke as an André Kostelanetz soundtrack played in the background. They eventually chalked it up as just another Russian "wild goose chase," and headed back to Toronto.

Gasparov also has the irritating habit of cloaking his all-consuming self interests in some Marxist bullshit about him acting "for the greater good," an argument that had always repulsed Brickman, whether it came from Moscow, Pyongyang, the Department of Homeland Security in Washington, or the CEO of General Motors. He is fond of saying, "Mr. Brickman, it is my job to deal on the basis of what is best for the Federation and for Russia's citizens."

But this time Brickman is prepared for "Stalin." He is developing a trap that even the Russian can't escape, and if he succeeds, it will devastate the Russians, perhaps bringing down Gasparov permanently.

Brickman clenches his right fist and brings it up to his chin. As he does he pauses to read at the inscription on his ring — *"Emitte lucem et veritatem"* — which encircles the symbol of a sun rising over water. "These few will help me," he thinks.

On Brickman's instruction, Molinari dials Chernoff in Dutch Harbor. The urgency of the ring tone rises with each waiting second. Molinari muses the mental arithmetic around the litigation in the wake of the sinkings, and the boon in billable hours to his firm. Typically, cases such as this go on for three to five years, and the firm might easily manage 2,000 to 3,000 annual billable hours at $250 to $650 per hour. This case alone could set him up for the next 24 months. Here's to rogue waves and the pitiless Bering Sea, he thinks.

"Mike?"

"Akna, it's Ryan. I'm in Seattle with Mike."

"A.C., we need to cover the tonnage from the two boats before 'Stalin' decides to raise the price on our Russian crab agreements. Get the word out that we're in the market for boats with quota, and we are willing to pay up for them."

"Ryan, is this real, or are you just chumming to get the Commies to think you're covering a bet?"

"They're all thinking that we're in trouble because of our losses, and I want to encourage that line of thought. Let the rest of the industry think that we're in a bind for crab, and slowly raise the grounds price and circulate that we are looking to replace the SIRIUS and the VEGA."

Chernoff thinks for a moment. "Listen Ryan, I know what you're thinking, but a few of the players will start asking questions, no doubt. I'm hearing that Tongbang Brothers has been buying heavy in B-Grade crab, and they've become more aggressive since the sinkings."

"Just give 'em the facts: Two boats gone. We're down by a third on our tonnage. And we're looking to cover it. But I guarantee you nobody will ask you. The story of the wreck is too big, too bulletproof. As soon as word hits that we are shopping quota, the market will take off. You know the way it works. Every player who's ever touched red crab will want to speculate in the market. Hell, I want every goddamn Piggly Wiggly store in Tuscaloosa buying king crab futures by the time it's over, and taking Tongbang with them. The deeper he's in the better."

"It's over," tolled ominously in Chernoff's brain. In this business, betting against the Japanese can have devastating repercussions. When it comes to the global seafood markets, the Japanese occupy a class all their own. With millennia of reliance on the sea for survival, fish commerce is a religion in Japan, and the companies chartered to manage the daily five million pounds that ebb and flow through Tokyo's Tsukiji market are virtual departments of the state, holding sway over government policy, and even the country's elected leadership.

Akiro Watanabe, the titular head of Daichi Umi, Japan's leading chartered seafood supplier, is a monthly guest on the "Imperial Household Agency," the post-WWII incarnation of the Imperial monarchy of Nippon. As a devotee of American business theory, Watanabe has often quoted Thor Veblen, the American economist who has written that the essential work of business is to continually advance commerce into areas previously understood as criminal. The geo-economic evolution of Japan has created a dependency on foreign marine protein production that verges on tyranny. Japanese fishing companies, scouring the planet for abundant fishing grounds, have built armadas of massive factory ships that can catch, process, and freeze staple supplies, all free of the constraints of land-based facilities. By mid-century, Japanese fishing companies had initiated the practice of cash payments to government officials to protect coastal fishing rights for their exclusive use. The unintended consequence is that the fishing fleets of the Rising Sun are victims of their own expedience. Coastal states are quickly recognizing the revenue opportunities created by extending their borders into the sea. The emergence of the 200-mile Exclusive Economic Zone was codified in 1982 by the United Nations' Law of the Sea Convention. The net effect is an explosion in local fishing industrialization, and the consequent collapse of the global Japanese fishing industry. In due course, the entire Japanese economy has suffered from the impact of a relentless inflation in seafood prices. On the heels of the back-breaking general inflation of the last century, it is becoming a struggle for the average Japanese citizen to afford fish.

A little frustrated, Chernoff says, "Ryan, are you out of your mind? With the Yen up, the Japs will buy every pound of Alaskan Red crab on the market, and I guarantee you that the Russians will stop shipping, and probably become buyers once they hear what Daichi and the rest of 'em are up to. There are only 100 days to execute on the retail contracts, and we haven't laid in even half of the tonnage we'll need to cover the orders."

Unphased, Brickman continues, "Send me the inventory of what's in stock in Seattle, along with how much Russian product we have in the Saigon zone. Then call your friend at statistics who files the weekly U.S. Cold Storage reports. I need a two-percent reduction in crab inventories every week for the next eight weeks. Get together with him and see what it will take to make it happen."

"Ryan, this guy is getting to be a very nervous cat. It used to be that I could bring him and his buddy up to Dutch to catch a couple of salmon, and he'd do anything for me. But since all of the Homeland Security stuff, he's becoming paranoid. To get him to shade the published inventory numbers is going to take cash. He wants $100 gift cards, can you believe it? I'm guessing 10K, at a minimum."

"OK. Take $9,900 in cash from the capital construction account. Post it to the system under 'Boat Parts.' Take the plane to Seattle and buy ten cards per store, two at a time, in ten different stores. Put them in a box of Marlboro's and have him meet you at the bar in the Hilton Garden Inn at SeaTac. There are no cameras there."

Brickman turns to Molinari. "Attorney client privilege, right Mike?"

Molinari nods his head in agreement. "Yes it is, but I caution you that it is only because Chernoff is a shareholder in the Alaskan corporation, and that I represent you acting on behalf of the officers of the company. Were he not a shareholder, that conversation would not be privileged, and it would not be protected if I were to be deposed or subpoenaed to testify in court. Ryan, as your attorney and a director of the corporation, I caution you against considering this course without consulting the full Board, as this action could have a material impact on the financial viability of the company. And, I remind you, any allocations from the capital construction account require approval of the Board. The same goes for any decision to replace the boats. Strictly speaking, the Board members need to vote on it, and, frankly, I suggest that, from the standpoint of financial risk, nothing should be done before receipt of the insurance claim. What if something goes wrong with the claim?"

Lesterman concurs, "Listen Ryan, I hate to say that I agree with the lawyer, but our cash requirement can be two to five million a day, depending on the weather and the landings. A price surge is going to make my life miserable with the bank, not to mention having to battle every skipper who calls in to unload for a higher price. Plus, there's the extra work that this will put on the weighmasters at the dock. You know what happens when the market starts climbing. Suddenly we are cheating every boat on the weight tag. They start bitching about the ice allowance that we use to discount the hoist weight, and there's another battle. My guys start calling me every time a boat pulls up to the hoist."

CHAPTER 17

It is Gare du Nord, and Melina Bunge deposits Jane for the Thalys train to Brussels.

Before Jane gets out of the car, Bunge recaps, "Based on our talk, I say that for F. Bunge to resolve the current issue for Seven Seas, we do so based on an hourly rate. As I've said, I expect 20 to 30 hours at 175 Euros per hour. Additional expenses will be for travel, on cost. I also expect 20 to 30 percent of the staff-hours, and I anticipate a single cash charge of about 1,000 Euros. I will send all this to you by e-mail this evening, if you will agree to have a decision to me by, say, the middle of next week." Before Jane can answer, "I forgot to ask you. What name will be on the bottom of the contract?"

"Yes, later next week. And for the signatures, put Ryan Brickman, Arthur Lesterman, and Jane Dreyfus. I'll reply to you by e-mail with the exact spellings."

Brickman requires the *hanko*[1] of each manager involved in implementing any decision by Seven Seas that exceeded $10,000. Over the course of his business dealings with the Japanese, he has become an adherent of *"ringi,"* their term for the consensus-decisioning process. He is convinced that the "bottom up" endorsement process actually speeds execution by eliminating foot-dragging, while also creating a culture of "shared fate" with an entire cohort. It is the shouldering of the outcome of a decision by the group, rather than the individual. The prevailing spirit of "We may all hang together, but we will hang separately" is pervasive, and gives everyone working for an organization an attitude of certainty that verges on defiance.

"Bon. And so that Bunge does not surprise you, let me repeat that we do not guarantee the result. So, the agreement term is a 5,000 Euro deposit, and the balance when we present the *dédouanement* — the customs release to Seven Seas. If there is no release, there will be no balance due, except the expenses. What are your questions?"

The two women discuss the scheduling of the reply around Jane's return trip through Denver on Wednesday. In closing the conversation, Jane says, "I can't promise a specific time right now. There are too many variables. But let's say by 'first thing' Monday I will call you with an update and any questions we might have."

---

1 Japanese term for a horn, wood, or stone seal imprinted with the bearer's name (like a signature to a Westerner). They are indispensable tools for Japanese adults in authorizing myriad transactions.

"Jane, I will ask you a strange thing, but I must ask it. What do I do if I hear nothing from you by Tuesday? If I call your cell what message can I leave for you so you call me back?"

Jane bristles at the question. What is it with this woman? Talk about compulsive! I have just told her that I will call her Monday. Jane decides that it's time for her to regain control of this conversation.

"Listen, Melina, if you don't reach me perhaps I am on the phone. Just call me back."

Melina squeezes her lips together as if she has tasted something bitter, then cocks her head to the right while rocking it somberly from side to side. "*Je suis très désolé*. I am very sorry, Jane, to tell you, but we do not call you back."

Jane gazes up at the magnificent arched, glass edifice of Gare du Nord, smiling and chuckling under her breath. "If I do not call you back, you have my permission to e-mail Ryan Brickman and tell him that I have not answered you. But don't worry. I will call you on Monday."

They agree to await the follow-up on Monday, and briefly chat about joining up again in Brussels, as time allows.

As Jane enters the train station she swoons slightly at the massive size and energy of the place. What is it about rail stations that make them so powerfully evocative, in a way no airport ever has affected her. Is it the immensity of the place? Is it the thought that, decade after decade, millions of people have passed through this place before her, each bearing some great expectation that only travel can enable? Soldiers off to battle. Sales folks out to change the world. Bogart searching for Bergman, hanging from the door of the rail car. "Is Paris Burning?"

Five thousand Euros is nothing, she thinks to herself. The real investment, the real risk, is to her credibility if F. Bunge fails to secure the release of the seized cargo, and things unravel. The 5,000 will just add insult to a huge injury. Not only had she initially championed the Southeast Asian business into France, she had managed the sales and sourcing. But now she essentially will be responsible for appointing F. Bunge to fix it, thus putting her business judgment on the line again. Can she sustain another hit? What would Brickman think? What would the Seven Seas Board think?

Jane settles into the "Comfort One" seat for the 90-minute ride to Brussels. She takes out a pen and legal pad and begins noodling the arithmetic on the cost of clearing the rejected goods. She draws three columns on the page and labels them "Worst Case," "Best Case," and "Most Likely Case," and begins entering the expenses. In the end, the figures are $1.2 million, $450,000, and $675,000. She has added a 20 percent contingency to each, because there are always unforeseen and unintended costs. She takes out her Blackberry and writes an e-mail to Brickman and Lesterman about the outcome of the meeting with F. Bunge, and the consequences she anticipates. One of the fundamental pleasures of working in top management at Seven Seas is that there is a "highliners" attitude of open and essential communications. If a fact can have material impact on the business, or there is the possibility for ambiguity, or any chance of being misunderstood (due to one assumption or another), or if it needs to be raised, there is a management policy that specifically selects against the "bearer of bad news" syndrome. If any crew member on a boat spots an issue that might jeopardize the operations of the boat, or the safety of the crew, he is obligated to report it immediately. This is the communications philosophy of the Seven Seas organization: Attention to detail, and a bias toward over communicating on issues that any member of the crew perceived as "money."

In this case, the investment in the F. Bunge engagement will cost, on the high side, $30,000, her maximum downside. And with Bunge's reputation on her side, the most likely case would be a recovery of well over half a million dollars on the loss. Best case could be as high as $800,000. In that light, assuming that Jane is confident that Bunge can deliver, which she is, the decision is a no-brainer. And she is certain that she can convince Brickman to see it her way and endorse the deal.

"Nous accélérons maintenant à vitesse maximum 250," the soft female voice announces over the intercom as Jane's body presses back into the seat cushion under the force of acceleration. She releases her neck muscles and her head gently rolls to the right, her forehead resting against the lateral headrest. What a comfortable design, what a comfortable life, she thinks. The thought, even the feeling, is strangely disturbing to her as her eyes slowly shut, shuttering her view of the brooding overcast coming in from the west over Normandy. "This good life is a gift to you. Do not take it for granted." She recalls her father's words. He had never made things easy for her, keeping her accountable for even the smallest duties. Without her mother, Jane was raised with little attention to feminine impertinences such as clothing, fashion, and make-up,

which her father had restricted with nearly draconian discipline. Instead of allowing her to waste time "teen-aging," as he called it, he had saturated her mind with readings from Viktor Frankl and Ayn Rand, hammering home the discipline that self-responsibility is first and foremost. He said that life's purpose is to deal exclusively with the unique challenges and opportunities that it presents to each of us as individuals, and that our only obligation is to the fidelity of the outcomes we create through the decisions and the actions we take as individuals. Also, we should create, based on our personal vision. We should reject dogma and the "herd mentality," and instead, ground ourselves in individualism, and in the belief of free will and self-determination. "If they're all going right, you go left," he would say. "Don't pray to God to help you, pray for you to help God." This is how the Dreyfus family behaved. Never be resigned to fate, even when the risks are high or the going is rough.

As the train speeds through the battle-hardened hills of the Ardennes, Jane recalls that these are the fields where her great grandfather had fought "the Hun." Pierre Dreyfus received the Croix de Guerre in WWI for courageous action, but it was his father, Capt. Alfred Dreyfus, an Alsatian Jew serving in the French army during the Franco-Prussian War, who gave prominence to her surname among the French. Capt. Dreyfus was arrested and convicted of treason in 1895, and was sent to the notorious French penal colony of Devil's Island, off the coast of French Guiana, where he nearly died of dysentery. He later returned to France to vindicate himself. His work finally paid off when evidence surfaced in the press that testimony against him had been falsified by a group of Jew-hating officers who had covered for the real traitor. The courts later acquitted Dreyfus and reinstated his rank and commission, but not before the Dreyfus Affair had acquired *"causes cé·lè·bres"* status, and revealed that France was not immune to the tide of anti-Semitism that had already chronically infected Germany. The story, covered exhaustively by the liberal press, polarized turn-of-the-century France around an issue that presaged the Nazi-enabled rise of the Vichy French during WWII.

From the time Jane was a small girl, her father had lectured her about the Dreyfus family legacy: tough-minded with fearless self-determination. The family had a tradition of facing challenges head on, and the enduring stories were in her blood. How Pierre, while he was attempting to cross the Meuse River to safety at Verdun, had saved the lives of seven wounded comrades who had come under attack. How his heroic, one-man assault had massacred a German patrol that would have certainly finished them off, had he not made the decision take swift action. How, after the war, he always refused to speak of the events of that day, briefly becoming a pacifist, at least until the Nazi's attack in the Sudan at the start of WWII (the same ground he had fought on just two decades before). And the stories of Pierre's father, suffering at the hands of the sadists at *Île du Diable,* yet battling for a retrial until finally being returned France and to freedom, even, in time, winning an appointment to the prestigious *"Ordre national de la Légion d'honneur."* Both men had put themselves on the line, investing everything on an outcome they apparently believed in, in spite of high risk, in spite of danger, even death.

What is she investing to achieve the outcomes that she is seeking, she wondered. Has she become too comfortable? Is her comfort slowly weakening her? Destroying her? It feels like the time has coming to make some decisions. To take risks that might be uncomfortable, even fearful. Perhaps there is no possibility for her to create anything important, anything original, anything that would have any permanence or impact without a deep-seated, relentless commitment to that which creates uncertainty, and is willfully disruptive. In short, it may be time to shake things up. The world is looking for "sure things," but sure things are not for Jane.

CHAPTER 18

"Jane, write down the following seven words."

"But David, I have some questions. I'm not sure I'm the right person for handling this presentation. After all, I wasn't in at the very beginning."

"OK, maybe you're not. Now what do you do? I call it a 'team sale.' It's not unusual for different stages of the process to be handled by different people. The same basic rules apply as long as communications are good. In this case you have been brought in as the decision-taker, as the collector. Some people call it a "closing," but I don't like the term for a number of reasons that we can talk about some other time. Your boss and his colleague have laid the ground-work for you. They are setting up an "investigation meeting with authority." You need to let go of the emotional part — the 'Am I the right person?' stuff. When you get emotional about the outcome of a conversation, they control you. If you get them emotional about the outcome, you control them."

"That's right. I always get in trouble with an account when I start thinking they are 'special' in some way. I stop handling them systematically and start thinking that I need to make an exception in their case. Whenever I get enthralled with a piece of business, it goes bad."

"Correct! That's a huge point, Jane. Emotions undermine our ability to think rationally. Rational thought and emotion simply cannot coexist. The only time that can be beneficial is when you are in mortal danger, and even then it can be problematic. You're feeling it now because somewhere deep down in your lizard brain you've perverted a connection linking presentations to limbic 'fight or flight.' Your emotions take over and shut you down."

"Right, I'm nervous about it, a little panicky. I've been in this position hundreds of times before: I'm about to do a presentation and nervous as hell, rifling through my deck, seizing up."

"Jane, it doesn't matter."

"What doesn't matter?"

"It simply doesn't matter. The outcome of this meeting simply doesn't matter."

"David, I'm sorry, but you're losing me. I really don't think this is helping me with my problem."

"Jane, let me ask you a question. Have you been successful in the past, doing what you do?"

"Well, sometimes, and sometimes I wonder . . ."

"Yes or no?"

"OK, the answer is, Yes."

"Are you sure? Are you confident in that answer?"

"Can we move on, please? That's my final answer."

"When you leave this presentation you will be the same successful person you have always been. Know this: The best predictor of future success is previous success. So, what I'm telling you is that there isn't a damn thing worth worrying about that justifies the fear or emotion you are layering onto this situation. You're not seeing the forest for the trees. You have already succeeded."

With that comment, Jane's mind began to clear. As she turns her view from the spinning pen barrel balanced in her fingers to the rolling hills beyond the railcar window, she briefly recalls herself in a child's countryside in northwestern Maryland. She remembers how the thunderstorms that blasted their way north by northwest up from the Chesapeake would chase her into the arms of her father, and the incredible relief of his embrace, and his reassurance that, "It's gonna to be OK, Kid-O." This is like that, she thought, but an even more powerful affirmation, because even though David is speaking the words, the truth is coming from somewhere deep inside her own sense of self-confidence. She knows she will prevail, regardless of the outcome.

"Jane, there's nothing in the world that can get in the way of your succeeding on this call. Period. So let's get back to the presentation. It's the last step in the Guess-Free Sales process — the confirmation step before the agreement. Many sales people think that the presentation comes first to allow them to 'show and tell' the prospect how wonderful they are. But it's a fatal mistake. If you stick with the GFS process — if you stick with the sequence and remain in control — by this stage you're approaching zero uncertainty about what the outcome will be. By the end of the presentation, the conversation is complete, and there will be nothing left undone except collecting the agreement. Is it logical that if you follow the sequence through — the presentation stage, challenging the unknowns, and making no assumptions — by that point it's a simple matter of 'I think we're done here. Check please.'"

"Of course. That makes perfect sense. If I've managed the expectations, if I've shown that I'm good at turning the telescope around and focusing on the prospect, there are no surprises. If I've asked the right people — the ones in authority — the reality-testing questions, and I've challenged them about the investment, and quantified the measurable payoff from our deal, I guess I deserve the agreement, right?"

"Guess you deserve it? I don't know the answer to that, but I think you know who does. But I never use the word 'deserve' in Guess-Free Sales because it's passive. It's totally irrelevant in deal making. Having the agreement in your hand is what matters. Remind me to talk with you about the sales person's Bill of Rights. One of them is: You have the right to ask for a signed agreement. There are different ways of asking that question, but you should be prepared to exercise it at any time you feel it's appropriate. Never 'assume,' never 'deserve.'"

"OK, so forget the fear and loathing over when to ask for the agreement. If I feel that the time has arrived go ahead and ask, correct?"

"Yes. Again, if you feel it, ask it. If you're feeling it, so are they. Worst case, they say 'No, were not ready,' and you continue on with the process."

"OK, got it. But I can tell you that I am going to have to do a presentation this time because it is formal part of the puzzle. I'm providing information about us that they need for them to make the decision."

"You need the presentation to consolidate the story of the deal, but it's not your story. It's their story. You are selling them back the outcome they have already told you they are looking to buy. Plus, you need to do a last dig to find that one important uncertainty that is still lying just below the surface that will wreck the deal."

"So there's always one more, huh? Maybe that explains why prospects go dark on me after I walk out of the presentation thinking that they loved me."

"It's called 'happy ears.' You walk into your office telling your boss how much they loved your stuff, and that it's a done deal. But the trouble is, you're dead wrong. You think it was a complete presentation, but it wasn't. You didn't give them chance to present to you, which, by the way, would have led to a decision right then and there. Instead you settled for a smile and a 'We'll get back to you shortly.' And the sad part is that a clue to that outcome probably floated out in a comment from one of the authorities while you were in between the slide titled 'How Big We Are!' and the one titled 'How Smart We Are!' And that clue was left right on the conference table right in front of you, unaddressed, as you all walked out joking about missing your flight because you went overtime."

"Can you feel my embarrassment over the phone?"

"Jane, if the prospect team is all smiles at the end of the presentation, it's actually a counter-indicator. They're trying to escort you courteously out of the building because they've decided that it's all about you. And that spells 'death to the deal.' When you come to the end of a presentation, you want to see sober faces all round, even looks of concern and caution. This is how people appear when they suddenly find themselves in a position where there are no uncertainties left, except for when, exactly, they are going to have to cut that big fat check to you!"

"I love that look!"

"Naturally. Then why settle for appeasement. Your job is to figure out what's in the way of getting the signature on the agreement, and obviate it."

"But, if there's a deal breaker out there, they must know what it is. Why not just tell me and get it over with."

"Remember this: There is no 'Geez, you didn't tell me that part?' in business. Whether or not the deal breaker is clear and present in the prospect's mind at the time of the presentation, they've learned that eventually one of your competitors will ask the right questions and figure it out. There's seldom a handout titled 'How To Sell Us,' so you need to learn to ask the questions."

The movie out the train window is suddenly like a 1950s foreign film in black and white. The train slows and begins a long roll out over Napoleon's final fields, cutting a red crescent in the hillside as the rail bed changes its heading from west to north, and on to the final approach into Bruxelles-Midi station.

"You have every right to an affirmative decision. When the presentation is over, you make the only assertion that is allowed in the GFS process: The presumptive 'Sign here please.' But first, take them to the mat. That done, you're at ease in putting out your hand, palm upward, and asking for the signed deal. And they will be perfectly at ease giving it to you. Reluctance-free sales, that's always the goal. Jane, I'm sending you an e-mail with the seven steps to a GFS presentation, which will deliver this result. Use it for the talk tomorrow and you won't need the Powerpoint. Let me know if you have any questions."

Jane retrieves her e-mails as the train approaches Brussels.

From: David Shepard
Sent: Wednesday, August 03, 2011 9:53 AM
To: Jane Dreyfus
Subject: GFS Presentation Steps

Opening	Quorum check, Set Expectation, Assess participants	"What does each want to hear?"
Agenda	Prepare one, request one.	"What would you like to add?"
Review	Recap priorities, dig for hidden issues.	"Why wouldn't this work?"
Presentation	The Outcome. Interactive sell them back their dream.	"Are you sure?"
Summary	The situation, their envisioned outcome, the bridge.	No marketing, just facts.
Q&A	Presume questions – bring your own.	Listen and dig.
Decision	Agreement now? Is it over? WWW is the next step?	"What's next?"

David Shepard, Principal and Coach
Guess-Free Selling, LLC

"Jane, I get these fellows. Let me tell you, they are all ego. You know what I am talking about, right? You will find them at the Grand Place tonight, drunk and chest slamming like they're a herd of reindeer. And this is a men's club you are walking into with the Icelanders, so they are 'Alphas.' Understand? But they are also very smart and they know business. Possibly not your business so much, but it is on the financial side that they are very sharp."

☙

CHAPTER 19

Brickman had told Jane to be expecting a call from Og Oskarsson, the Icelandic counsel in New York City. Brickman had met Oskarsson at an industry conference in Reykjavik, and sharing a no-nonsense penchant for deal-making and Scandinavian women, they struck up a quick and collegial friendship. Iceland's prominence in the seafood industry provided it with important common ground, and Oskarsson's high-altitude view of the larger dynamics at work in the economy was intriguing to Brickman. Oskarsson had been instrumental in creating the current buzz about Iceland in the U.S. banking and investment communities, and had built the channels of dialog between Wall Street and Reykjavik.

"Saga" class on the two o'clock Icelandair flight out of JFK has become a prized booking as banks, investment funds, and various high-net-worth individuals made the pilgrimage, seeking higher yields and an obligatory soaking in the geothermal mud baths at Hveragerdi.

With a population fewer than 500,000, there is a limited argument for domestic market expansion opportunities in Iceland itself. But through an odd commercial version of the Easter Island effect, the

Icelanders have skillfully adapted to their rather unusual mix of rigid geo-economic constraints, tough-headed self-determinism, and incestuous business culture to yield a peculiar strain of high-risk entrepreneurial spirit. They are movers, and true to their Nordic ancestry, are inherently bent on deal-seeking. Coming from such a remote, sparsely populated, and resource-poor country, Icelandic deal-makers are often found at any important banking or investment venue. Their distinctly Aryan boldness and ubiquity has provided a unique niche for Icelandic banks as intermediaries in the arbitrage between conservative western banks and emerging markets, where the commercial risk level is "outside the envelope." Eastern Europe has become an important client base for Iceland's banks, and it was the risk equation in the post-Glasnost period that made Iceland an prime commercial portal for the new Russian Federation.

Oskarsson has described to Brickman, in detail, the inflationary currency situation in Iceland, and how global bankers, overloaded with U.S. dollars, had zeroed in on Iceland as a sexy spot to advise their clients to park surplus greenbacks. He explained the absurdity of investment banking, where millionaire bankers create investments for oblivious billionaire clients, hatched out of thin air by the creative geniuses from Princeton and Harvard and MIT, with thin foundation in economic reality.

"They create the markets, they inflate the markets, and then they short the very markets they created. That, in a nutshell, is the underlying purpose of Goldman Sachs. Like one of those circus sideshow money machines for the very, very rich," Oskarsson said. "The world is stuck with dollars, Ryan. It's somewhat ridiculous. We are only 400,000 people, and they want to build us new infrastructure, airports, hotels, spas, everything. Actually there are limitations here, you understand. Not all of these funds can be absorbed here."

He went on to described the curious cash dilemma of Iceland's bankers, who are in need of large dollar-based "exvestments" to maintain the flow of investment cash entering the country. They need to move dollars. So the financing or acquisition of a U.S. seafood company would be just such a perfect opportunity, custom made for an Icelandic bank with vast seafood-industry knowledge.

To Brickman, the timing is perfect. Some of the big banks in the U.S. are trimming their commercial banking due, in part, to significant loan losses being posted in the real estate sector. As the Seven Seas business grows, he is finding it increasingly difficult to expand his line of credit. The bank had recently requested that he pledge his personal real estate holdings as additional security on the asset-based line of credit. Though Brickman has no interest in selling the company, he is flexible about considering any financing arrangement with the Icelanders that will provide liquidity, as long as it had a neutral or negative impact on Seven Seas blended cost of capital.

"Og," Janes says, "I don't know much about the financial options. I am not the money person. You will need to talk with Ryan on that. I am here to present information regarding the marketing side of the business, and some background on the operations and Ryan's goals for the financing."

"Jane, I understand. But you now have a bigger role here. This is kind of a movie, you know what I mean? You are not trying to sell these fellows. You know they are already sold, or they wouldn't have invited your presentation. You are acting as a guide to help them arrive at an outcome that they already are looking to achieve, which is signing a term sheet for Seven Seas funding."

"Listen, I understand what you are saying, Og. But I have this Powerpoint presentation that I normally use for customers. I've made some changes, but it talks about the history of the company, something about Ryan, the plants . . ."

"I understand that this is how you normally sell, correct? But this situation is not peddling fish." He smiles, breaking into a percolating laugh that he cuts off by biting his lower lip. "I'm sorry. You know we actually have the internet in Reykjavik? The bank has already checked out Seven Seas in every way possible. Hell, they could probably tell you your bra size, yaah. You know what I am saying, don't you?"

Jane grins with unoffended passivity at his versed comment, writing it off to enculturation. Her mind drifts momentarily. Her eyes shift down and to the left as her brain flashes to the press that her company's bankruptcy received, all over the internet. The stories that circulated in the trade press about her mismanagement, and her over dominance of the Board of TradeRaider, which resulted in the company's downfall. Could this come back to haunt her now, years later?

"Jane, I have arranged dinner tonight with the CEO and Chairman of the Board of Islandbanc. His name is Magnus Krisuvik. He speaks fluent English, and is a very easy person to talk with. Your job is not to sell him on Seven Seas, but to learn his mind instead. What is he looking to accomplish with the Seven Seas funding, from the money and risk side? Let him explain it to you, then you'll have him. He will have some questions about the business, and about you and Hoffman, etc. But you need to come back always to what he needs for him to be comfortable with issuing the term sheet. Here's the idea. When you do the presentation on Monday, you give them the Powerpoint, yaah, yaah, yaah. But also we will take his comments from tonight and add them into the presentation. Remember, in your the presentation 'about Seven Seas' you are actually selling him back the outcome they are looking to achieve. You understand?"

"Listen Og, I know Ryan, and he's not going to go for this. There are some bank conditions that he will never agree to, like pledging personal assets, and some that I can't address with any authority at all, at least not without discussing it with Ryan first."

"Yes, and when you are in that position, and you're asked that kind of question, what does your instinct tell you to say?"

"In the first case, 'No,' and in the second 'I don't know.'"

"Exactly. You should say the same thing here. They will respect you if you are deliberate in your answers. They won't trust you if they think you are sucking up, yaah."

Jane is feeling more and more confident about her talk. She's a straight talker who loathes indirectness. If Oskarsson is right, this is going to be her kind of audience.

"So we are calling this a presentation, yaah? But we are really selling them back their own vision of the this deal. But you begin by standing your ground. Right up front, talk about the requirements that don't make sense from the Seven Seas side. No surprises, you understand?"

"Right. Well, I think . . . Christ wait 'til I talk with Ryan. I need to get clear on the numbers again. Og, I'll need you to be my Icelandic banking expert in this meeting on Tuesday, OK? If I feel like I'm getting out of my element, I am going to toss it to you. But don't take the lead unless I give it to you. And after you've said your part, toss back to me, OK?"

"OK, OK. Yes, absolutely I will. But one more thing about your approach. Understand me, yaah. You want to be negative."

"Negative? What are you saying? I'm a salesperson, and no sales person is negative. It's the opposite of what the prospect wants to hear. These fellows are expecting me to be professional, right. Up, smiling, sunny disposition. My normal charming self!"

She smiles demurely, as if they are talking face to face. Straightening her posture, she tosses back her head and casually grooms her hair with the fingers of her right hand.

"Jane, the Board is all "D" personality guys, yaah, except for the new female President of Commercial Lending. I have not met her.

For the others, I know it is about being bright and brief with them. Few details. They want the big facts and the numbers. How Seven Seas will be good for their business. They respect pushing back. If they are positive about the outcome, you be neutral. If they are negative about an element of the deal, or the prospects for a particular part of the agreement, you should be even more negative, more conservative."

"Og, what if they say, 'It's a deal!,' right there on the spot, and accommodate all of Ryan's demands?"

"First, that won't happen because these bankers aren't like the other people you deal with in your business. They will think it over, everything, for a long time. Second, maybe they confirm something, maybe any single part of the deal, then you need to challenge it, you understand? Say, 'Are you sure?' Keep pressing them. Listen, I know the way these Icelanders think. It's like fishing. If you jerk the line too soon, when the fish is taking only little bites at the bait, the fish will run and be gone. But if you gently pull back he will chase the bait and bite down harder on the hook. Then when you set the hook, he is caught, and he can't get off."

৬

CHAPTER 20

Akiro Watanabe stands at the 7 o'clock position in a circle of buyers as the auctioneer grunts out the call price on a massive bluefin tuna that's lying on the pallet at his feet. This is a ritual that he and his family have shared over the last 122 years, and each morning at 5 o'clock he walks to the edge of the circle to reconnect with the DNA of that legacy. There's the familiar barking voice of the auctioneer and the whining-clanking of the tow motors. There's the fresh cucumber smell of the fish as the pre-dawn Sagami breeze rolls in over the market floor.

Back when he first entered the business, there was honor for his family and his industry. Seafood was king, and every top graduate from the Tokyo Stock Exchange scrambled to become part of the royalty of *sakana*.[1] But a confluence of forces has conspired to undermine the power of the "big three" dynasties that have controlled the trade for centuries. In Watanabe's mind, the mortal blow to the greater industry has been the decline of the Japanese fishing fleet. Japan was master of her own fate when she fished the world's seas without constraint. And thought the Imperial Navy was lost in WWII, the ocean-going fleet bore evidence that Japan still dominated the seas in a larger economic sense. Now, the old

---

1 A Japanese term referring to food eaten as an accompaniment to alcohol.

business structure of controls is unraveling. Japanese retailers have even taken to cutting out fishing companies like his own in an effort to reduce costs and streamline the supply chain. They have learned from Walmart that inefficiencies in sourcing and supply chain can no longer be tolerated in the new millennium market. And Japan itself seems to be fading under the same setting sun as his fishing industry, which, to his mind is unacceptable. He feels in his soul that it is time for Japan to reassert its dominance over seafood globally. It is time to show that only they have sufficient market clout to move markets and, like DeBeers in the diamond trade, dictate the prices that are paid as well as control supplies. All he needs is the opportunity.

Ryan Brickman gazes out the window of the 737-700 as it climbs steeply above the east bay, then banks to heading 270 and around the waterfront of San Francisco. The resolution of the sky is crystal clear, and he can just make out the details in the compassed grid of buildings and streets below.

"You are now free to use electronic devices." He notes the spire of the Ferry Building and the Embarcadero, where he roamed as a teenager. The cash he collected unloading fishing boats and working scab near the stevedores union hall had funded his first motorcycle, a beat-up 1967 Norton Commando. At times there was night work, "replacing" shipments that had been seized for customs violations, or helping with an "express delivery" of goods whipped from the bulk carriers before the days of containerized freight.

He can just make out the spot where the Eagle Café once stood. The Eagle was the 1924 bastard merger of a 24-hour breakfast hall and bucket-o-blood saloon. Hanging over the 50-foot mirrored (and formerly red) walnut bar was a professionally framed black-and-white blow-up of a head shot on three horses, veins bulging, nostrils dilated, necks over-extended, and lips gently touching a thin white line that cut diagonally across photo. The inscription below read: "Only Triple Dead Heat to Win – Aquaduct, June 10, 1944." For some reason, Brickman felt like he was born under that photograph, like he'd bought a ticket to win on all three horses. He was born, he has thought many times, just plain lucky.

The Eagle served the dock workers breakfast and mugs of thick coffee from five in the morning to 11 at night, from a self-serve kitchen and cafeteria tables that filled the room, which was the size of half a basketball court. He recalls the beef he once got into on the steps of the Eagle while on a break one December morning. One of the crab boat skippers from the wharf had confronted him, accusing him of stealing a bin of live crabs that had been soaking under the pier in fish alley, off Jefferson Street. Brickman and a buddy had towed it off with a skiff, and sold it to a competitor down on the dock for cash. Because the dust-up remained civilized and finally broke up, he thought he had charmed his way through. But the next day, while he worked on the market floor shoveling flake ice up into a bin of salmon, the same highliner casually approached him from the alley. As Brickman turned to face the guy, resting on the shovel, the fisherman reached up and gently stroked his face with an open palm, as if in some strange gesture of forgiveness. He felt a barely detectable stinging sensation, which he figured was the scratch from the rope-broken callouses that fill the claws that most fisherman pass off as hands. But as the man suddenly jogged to the right and away from him, he could see in the stunned faces of those standing nearby that something was wrong. The chest of his khaki shirt suddenly blossomed with a bouquet of red drops and, reaching to his cheek, he felt the warm blood running down his ice-frozen hand and into the forearm of his union suit sleeve. His attacker had employed a Sicilian street tactic of taping a razor blade between his ring and middle ringer, and with the fresh edge of the blade exposed he had sliced Brickman's cheek open from just below his left eye to the corner of his mouth. It was a neat quarter-inch deep incision, eventually leaving a permanent pencil-thin scar paralleling his jaw-line. It was nearly one year later that the crab boat was found capsized off the coast of the Farallones with no hands aboard. Though the area is a favorite fishing spot for crab and rock cod, it also has the heaviest concentration of white sharks east of the Great Barrier Reef. And it is a forgone conclusion that no boat going down in the Farallones was likely to yield survivors.

Brickman's trip to Portland is to visit with Hak Maruhan, the owner of a small trading company in the East Bay that has a long and storied history with Daichi Umi and Mr. Watanabe. As a young Tokyo banker, Maruhan was deployed to San Francisco with a team to open a commercial branch to serve the multitude of Japanese business owners between Los Angeles and Seattle. They all maintain strong business connections to the Japanese mainland. Maruhan's love of anything American, his charming personality, and his self-effacing manner generated a fast following in the agri-business segment, and even among his competitors in the Bay Area banking community. His relationship with Daichi Umi began from a chance invitation to the San Francisco consulate dinner to honor Akiro Watanabe. Their common interest in all things American soon blossomed into a conversation about shared business ambitions. Maruhan longed to have his own company in the U.S., so he had obtained a green card and remained in California. Watanabe longed to have direct customers for Daichi Umi in the U.S., a potentially huge market for his products, as well as an important hedge against the great shift in control brought on by the United Nations Convention. In particular, Watanabe wanted to develop a direct business relationship with Newday Stores. As one of America's largest retail groceries, with a footprint predominantly in the west, it seemed a perfect beachhead for the ground swell in seafood consumption that would mean the increased supplies aimed at the aging baby-boomer generation. Watanabe recognized that Maruhan was the ideal candidate for facilitating his plan, and after several follow-up meetings and careful solicitations at Newday, the two men struck a deal. Daichi Umi set up Maruhan in the business of running a stand-alone trading company. It is essentially a U.S. sales front with Carl Christian, Newday's vice president of protein procurement, as a very silent partner. Christian justified running much of Newday's seafood purchasing through Maruhan as a strategic sourcing play to leverage the Japanese access to high-quality seafood at low cost. The deal soon expanded to include Newday's vice president of merchandising, and consequently, the grocery chain soon became known for its national leadership in first-rate seafood, long before it became a nationwide trend.

Maruhan also acted as a purchasing agent for Daichi Umi, and whenever a man was needed on the ground to help resolve company issues in the states, Watanabe learned to rely on him. He has become a true-trusted advisor, although he often refers to himself as little more than a tour director for Daichi Umi executives who visit San Francisco from time to time to party.

Brickman knows differently. He knows through conversations with Watanabe himself that Maruhan's relationship is different. He is a highly placed and influential member of the company cognoscenti, and a confidant of Watanabe. Brickman knows that his legendary reputation for confidentiality makes him the natural go-between for enlisting Watanabe and Daichi Umi as a partner in Brickman's successful scheme to short the bay herring roe market. But this game will have far higher stakes. Presenting his idea successfully — and gaining agreement with the Japanese — will require more than a brilliant plan. Even though Brickman is confident that he understands the motivations and Machiavellian bent of the Daichi Umi leadership, he also recognizes that the magic to winning them over, and keeping them from ambushing Seven Seas itself, will be his arranging that the bearer of his initial communiqué must be someone Watanabe sees as unassailable and above reproach. It has to be someone whom they could never betray, in honor and for his years of allegiance.

"Ryan, this is crazy. Let me tell you, I don't know if Daichi will even discuss this." Maruhan raises his eyebrows and lowers his chin to his chest in an over-dramatized look of concern and foreboding. He casts his eyes in Brickman's direction in a half-bowed position of dread respect. Still, there's a twinkle in his eye. There's a look of excitement at the prospect of being part of something this important, of being called into a secret conversation by one he admired, Ryan Brickman. Hell, he had even named his own son Ryan, an assertion that Brickman never believed, but found flattering none-the-less. Maruhan also admitted that he chose the name, in part, because of his worship of the famous pitching Texan.

"I want you to tell Watanabe that I am planning on shorting the king crab market. But I can't do it alone. We must coordinate the effort. The two of us can, and the combined market power of Daichi and Seven Seas can bring the market to its knees. We are already at a cyclical high market. It's at a tipping point. The loss of my two boats has set the scenario in motion for a hyper-extended market, and I intend to take full advantage of it. I also want you to tell him that if he decides to work with me, I will assure him that one-half percent of the profits made on the Seven Seas' side of the short will go to him personally. Hak, I want you to be the banker on this deal. You have the connections in Japan. You know where to put the money. We have crab stocks off shore and will arrange to pay Watanabe from offshore accounts. There will be no possible way to trace the funds. I don't need to tell you that there will be ample opportunity for you to benefit as well. What do you say?"

"Listen Ryan, I'm going to tell you truthfully, OK? I am your friend, so nothing here is for my benefit, you know? I don't want anything from this. And I'm not saying that this will work. I tell you that I will take nothing. You understand? I must tell you honestly one other thing. Mr. Watanabe is very conservative. Do you know? He is very careful person. Not like the other Japanese guys, the crazy guys who are coming into king crab business with the cash, like the Kiki guy up in Seattle. You know, the guy with the machine guns that he shoots into Puget Sound from his back door. That guy is criminal, you know? Dangerous guy. *Yakuza.*"[2]

"Hak, relax. I'll make sure you are covered, and I'll protect Watanabe completely. We are in Vietnam, and we have accounts to make distributions anywhere in the world."

2   Traditional organized crime syndicates in Japan.

"I understand. First he will not take the money, I think. I do not know for sure, but I suppose not. But, if it is a good business opportunity for Daichi Umi, he will take it."

"Hak, the buying power of Seven Seas and Daichi Umi is 45 to 50 percent of the combined North Pacific crab production from the entire season, U.S. and Russian. The current market price is 170 percent of its 60-month moving average, and is approaching its 1983 record number. Everyone in the fishery knows that Seven Seas is in short supply, and that we will be in the market aggressively. The Russians are already complaining that they don't have enough crab to supply our repack. Of course, they're lying, but that's the official word from 'Stalin.'"

"I can tell you that Daichi's people say that the Russian's Barent Sea output is down by half. This leaves the Bering Sea and North of Japan. That's all for the Russians, plus whatever they can steal from the high seas fishery."

"We are immediately going to start aggressively bidding on the plants we have out in the Aleutians, and I've already spread the word that we are looking to replace the boats, and to put in market orders with any additional boats that want to sell to us. Of course, we will initiate these actions, but that's all."

"Ryan, the inventories are climbing. The retailers will see the numbers and push back on the price."

"We've got that covered, as well. There will be a steady drop in the reported inventory figures over the next 60 days. Once the print finally spikes in October, the retailers will already have booked their orders, and the food service and restaurant side will have already stocked inventories for the quarter."

Maruhan looks slightly puzzled. "What about Captain's Cabin? If we are talking about a normal season, we are looking at eight to ten million pounds from Alaska, plus another ten million from the Russians."

"The plan is that Watanabe will have his people float a statement in the trade press that Japan will take three quarters of the Alaska production this season. That's about 35 million pounds. We've put the word out that we already have half the retail business in place, and that they have booked more than 30 million pounds. Captain's Cabin is running an eight-week promotion over the holidays, and that will be good for 10 to 15 million pounds, which means that every rinky-dink chain will coat-tail once their national TV ads start running. So you can double that number. That totals 100 million pounds, and it doesn't even count the Europeans."

"Ryan, you are smart to work this out. But maybe others don't understand the situation like you do."

"Believe me, Hak, every producer and retailer is doing the same arithmetic that I am. They'll figure out that king crab is already over sold, even on a peaking market."

"I don't know the numbers like you do. You are smart. Why short the market if demand is strong like you tell me? Mr. Watanabe will want the market to go up if he is buying, no matter what the price is."

"Hak, it's market physics. Listen. Prices have cycles, and at the tops and bottoms of those cycles, supply and demand really don't matter. It's the price cycle that drives everything. Prices naturally increase on everything, then top off and go the other way and bottom out. No matter what the product is — the market DNA of each is different — the same law applies. I don't care if its apples or Google stock. We are topping in king crab, and the other fundamentals don't matter compared to the physics of the market. What goes up comes down. There's no other way it can go."

"So, what is your plan, then?"

"I will tell you my plan, but first I need you to talk with Watanabe and get an understanding of his mind on king crab this year. You understand? I need to know what his personal motivations are for this season. What he has committed to his Board, to the keiretsu, and how flexible he is, personally, to listening to my plan. Do you understand? I need to know what outcome he sees, right now, for the season before I can present my plan to him. Otherwise, if I fail to make it fit his vision of the future, he will reject it. So I must know his mind on this. Then we will talk. Can you do this?"

"I will call him now. He is just now at Tsukiji. I can reach him now."

The gentle vibration of Akiro Watanabe's cell phone breaks the spell of his morning meditation with the blue fin mantra pulsing on and on in the auctioning background. He steps from the circle and into the open alley adjacent to the main building, catching the sun-washed smell of fish-free air that's sweeping past the door.

"Watanabe-san, I beg your kind forgiveness for my call at this hour. I am very humble in asking you that you would provide me with a very few minutes to discuss something of great importance to you and to Daichi Umi, I believe."

Though Brickman has no idea what Maruhan is saying, he listens carefully for any inflection in his voice that might inform the responses from the other end, 16 hours ahead. Maruhan initially speaks in a low, deferential tone. Then he raises the volume and slows the pace, as if Watanabe is having trouble hearing or understanding him. He is monotone, but there is a distinct smile in his voice, as if to convey some pleasure of honor with the conversation he is having and with the message he is delivering. Then there is a growing authority, perhaps an assertion of truth about the certainty of what he is saying. He is extending vowels, ending phrases, as when making an assertion while seeking affirmation from a listener. As he continues talking, his pace quickens and his speech becomes more certain, with quick, chopped, single-syllable responses. The tone then changes again to soberly confident, as though something of gravity has been decided. His face turns from smile to grim resolve. He now bears some larger responsibility, and wants to be precise on all the details. Then suddenly, nothing. A long pause, followed by a few minutes punctuated by multiple "hi-hi-hi . . ." Maruhan covers the phone and slowly turns to Brickman.

"He will meet with you to discuss your plan in Maui on Saturday, and he has requested that there be no written communications about this meeting. Do you agree?"

Brickman nods, drawing his lips tightly around his teeth in a way that Maruhan can't tell if he is agreeing reluctantly, or if he is stifling a smile.

"Hak, I have one condition for Watanabe." Maruhan hesitates as he draws the cell phone up to his lips and begins to speak. He takes a deep breath. "Tell him that he must bring Mika with him."

A smile spreads across Maruhan's face, from his eyes to the corners of his mouth, as he begins speaking with a voice of restrained pleasure that quickly erupts into staggered laughter. Somewhere in the *hiragana* soup of Maruhan's reply, Brickman hears the name "Mika." The humor shared by the three centers on the fact that, because he will not speak English, Watanabe never travels on foreign business without Mika. Though he understands the English perfectly, and is a great fan of America and Americans, he refuses to communicate in English, or in any language other than Japanese. Instead, he relies on his multi-lingual personal interpreter, Mika Vargas, a Peruvian-Japanese beauty who accompanies him on foreign travels, serving as his constant mouthpiece to non-Nipponese. Mika's presence enlarges the experience of any meeting. Where Watanabe's manner is often serious and brooding, and can be intimidating to even the most seasoned business veteran, Mika, in contrast, is elegantly warm and disarming. Her remarkable talent for listening and keeping a presence of mind to the speaker was uncanny. Her seemingly flawless translation is always evidenced in each response back from Watanabe. While moving each conversation forward in a productive way, Watanabe is always truly coherent, on topic, and to the point.

☙

CHAPTER 21

Puakana House overlooks Kapalua Bay on Maui, on the edge
of the Emerald Golf Course. The jeep bounces along the Hana
coastal road on an unusually cool and overcast mid-morning.
Maruhan looks quickly over at Brickman, taking in a snapshot of
his profile set against the bay, before turning back to the view up
and over the conserved coastal ridge and the golf links beyond.
Maruhan is a fan of the mid-century artist Edward Hopper, and
the "drive by" stylization of detail that was common in his work.
This is the essence of Ryan Brickman, he thinks to himself — an
impression of motion, even when sitting still. Eyes squinting,
thoughts lost behind his dark-green aviator's glasses, chestnut
salt-and-pepper hair streaming out behind his beard, as if posing
for the cover of OUTSIDE or ALPINIST.

Maruhan idolizes Brickman. He seems the epitome of the
American ethic. Tough-minded, iconoclastic, independent,
ruggedly self-directed. And with the charisma of a natural-born
leader, but with none of the pontification or displays of
self-importance. If there are internal struggles with being Ryan
Brickman, they are seldom on display to the rest of the world.

Maruhan sees Brickman as unflappable, regardless of the inconvenience. He always appears to be remarkably comfortable and at ease with himself, regardless of the circumstance.

Early in their acquaintance Maruhan and Brickman shared a flight together from San Francisco to Los Angeles to visit Bill Broward, of Fortune Stores. Because of a thunderstorm just off the runway to the east, the plane was grounded for several minutes on the taxiway. As Maruhan read his newspaper, Brickman sat tapping on the face of his Submariner wristwatch. (His attention to timeliness is legendary. He is predictably early for every meeting, and detests tardiness in anyone or anything.) The captain had come on the intercom with several apologies about the delay, and Brickman's growing impatience was apparent with every tap of the intercom toggle. Suddenly the engines began spooling up, and with a quick warning from the cockpit that it was going to get "a little bumpy," the plane rolled into takeoff position and began to accelerate down the runway. The rain was heavy, and from the moment the plane began rotation it was buffeted by wind drafts, pressing up and then down on the lift as the jet crabbed to the left. As if starving to find airspeed, the engines screamed in the background. The wind sheer had not dampened with altitude, and within five minutes of takeoff it was slamming the plane violently. Though it was mid-morning, through the windows was an opaque, dusk-grey, punctuated by navigation-light discharges set in the deep cover that lit up like intermittent Christmas lights flashing through thick layers of dark angel hair. The mood in the cabin was palpably anxious, with cries coming up in unison with each hard dip and twist.

Suddenly a very loud explosion sucked all sound from the cabin, as if the immensity of it had momentarily neutralized the acoustic properties of the air. A ball of flame appeared from somewhere in front of the bulkhead, and rocketed down the aisle and out the rear. The plane bucked like a steer, then shuddered repeatedly before slowly regaining its stability and resuming its "bumpy" ascent. After the initial screams there was stunned silence. The captain came on soberly and confirmed that the plane had suffered a lightning strike, adding that it was harmless to the aircraft. He apologized for the severity of the turbulence. Within a few minutes the bumps began to settle out as the plane crested the cloud tops and flew into a perfectly clear, sapphire sky. It was a poetically poignant transition after the events of the previous 15 minutes. The clouds just below were as rich and white as whipped cream, while back to the west, off the starboard wing, a large blown-out, anvil-shaped cloud towered above them. In front of the plane, a few miles off to the east, the trailing edge of the storm was just coming into view with the altitude. At once, the flight attendants were up from their seats, followed by a number of pings on the intercom light, hailing the cabin crew from the cockpit.

The crew began moving with more urgency, one attendant running past Maruhan from the back of the plane clutching a red overnight bag. The plane began descending, gently at first, then with increasing urgency. The captain came back on intercom, his voice oddly calm and relaxed as he announced that the instruments were indicating a loss hydraulic pressure, and "We are descending as a precaution and rerouting the flight to an alternate airport." With that, the plane banked deeply to the right and began descending.

Chaos spread through the cabin, and the woman next to Brickman grabbed his arm, insistent that he explain to her what was going on. "Are we going to crash?" Maruhan recalled later that Brickman calmly responded to his panicked seat mate, saying that the descent was merely a precaution. The lightening strike had probably zapped one of the gauges. The hydraulic systems in planes were invulnerable to lightning strikes.

With the plane in rapid spiraling descent, Maruhan watched in amazement as Brickman proceeded to casually remove his wallet from his jacket pocket, at the same time he removed the satellite phone from the seat back in front of him. After swiping his American Express card, he began dialing the keypad.

Broward was at his desk in the LA distribution headquarters, studying inventory printouts when he lifted the receiver to hear Ryan Brickman's baritone voice resonate his name through the ear piece. What followed was an earnest apology that he was going to be late for their appointment, due to "a little problem with the plane" that had caused a change in the flight plan. He added that as soon as he was on the ground he could make alternate arrangements, and he would call back to reschedule the appointment later in the day.

"Later in the day?" Broward was incredulous, but he agreed to hold the afternoon open for Brickman, who, good to his word, arrived within four hours of their originally scheduled time. After they had landed, Brickman hired a charter from Fresno to Los Angeles.

He had casually mentioned to Maruhan as they stepped off the chartered plane that other than this Broward meeting and one other, he had never been late to a business appointment.

Maruhan cranks the steering wheel of the jeep into the driveway marked with nothing more than a burnished bronze plaque bolted into the ox-blood-red lava stone monument that forms the gate to the gravel lane. The plaque bears a stylized image of a sun rising over a rippling sea. The building is a mass of lines and planes — more an architectural drawing than a building. Three terraces vault up with increasing dimension, and cantilever from the gentle cliff face windward and east southeast, overlooking both the southern leg of Kalahu Beach and, further to the south, the cloud forest of Koolau. Glass supports the pumice-stone concrete rather than vice versa. The design of the building captures the essence of the phrase "unencumbered view."

They are met at the entrance to a narrow courtyard door by a tall, but modestly postured, woman dressed in a white-linen kimono and a amber silk top with a golden tread. She leads them down a hallway to an entryway that opens into a high-ceilinged room that looks out of the main level to ceiling glass and teak windows. Beyond lies a broad terraced balcony that steps down to a rectangular swimming pool that, from their vantage point, appears seamless with the grey sun-dusted Pacific beyond. At the woman's request, they remove their shoes and she leads them into the main living area. The room — the entire building, actually — exudes Zen: spare to the extreme, with no sign of the standard "Polynesia" that adorns even the most upscale accommodations throughout the Hawaiian vacationland. The room itself is "spartan Nippon." It is the most aesthetic and elegant of imperial interiors, in perfect harmony with the stratified stone throughout the entire building. There are five buckskin leather club chairs, the same amber color as sun over water on the entrance gate. The color is emblematic on all things in the Daichi Umi domain. The chairs are arranged evenly around a circular tea table that seems part of the deep pressed bamboo hardwood floor.

Brickman takes a seat just to the right of where he expects Watanabe to sit. Maruhan sits to Brickman's right, and both are facing the open glass and linen curtains that open onto the balcony. The trade winds, which left days before from Sonora or Santo Domingo, move in and about the room, enriching the native texture of the place. The sense is that the building grew on this spot from the vitreous and jungle that surround it.

Watanabe enters the room with his interpreter, Mika Vargas, to his right and close in his wake. As they step in the circle he bows to the two men before taking a seat to the left of Brickman, with Vargas between them. Vargas greets Brickman in English and Maruhan in Japanese, but Watanabe does not speak. The room falls to silence as they sit at attention facing each other. Brickman has had many business meetings with Japanese leadership, but Watanabe's are always different.

He recalls their first encounter during a visit to Fukuoka for the Fugu festival. As they were preparing to depart from a meal that included heavy drinking, skewered fingers, and sushi, Watanabe suddenly approached him, grasped his lapel and reached for the box of cigarettes Brickman had just put in his jacket pocket. After opening the box and seeing only three remaining smokes, Watanabe motioned to a lieutenant, who promptly produced a fresh pack of Dunhills, which Watanabe slipped casually into Brickman's jacket pocket. On the way to the car, Watanabe gestured with a frown at Brickman's coat collar, which he had haphazardly turned inside out while wrestling the coat on in his semi-sober state. Watanabe stood before him in the slow rain, carefully redressing the collar properly along the pleat line, then giving it a Batman's dusting off with the back of his hand before turning away and leaving without a word.

Though he can be deferential, even intimate, in a casual setting, when it comes to business conversations, Watanabe brings an almost monastic mood to any gathering. He will open each meeting with a prolonged silence, perhaps to help bring some order and clarity, and to clue the room to pay close attention to the next moment. Brickman has often wondered if it is a kind of warning that the promises made will be remembered and weighed against future actions. When Watanabe does speak, he seldom smiles, or even raises or changes the pace of his vocality, as if he is carefully dictating each unalterable word for inclusion in a permanent record. Vargas' translations always have the same somber meaning that his tone suggests, but her smile adds a natural musicality. That smile has the power to make the deadliest of messages sound lyrical.

This type of conversation isn't Brickman's natural style at all, but he none-the-less honors the ritual formality of their meetings, particularly today. After all, they are Watanabe's invited guests, and are considerate of the importance of all that is at stake.

· · · · · · ·

Brickman's behavior hasn't always been so honorable with his Asian customers. He is an infamous showman, known for outrageous behavior in meetings with the Japanese, who annually travel to his office in Seattle to negotiate crab and salmon prices. One oft-related story tells of Brickman being in a particularly contentious preseason negotiation with the crab buyers. The buyers were intent on driving the export price lower, while the Alaskan boat owners were convinced that the market was headed the other way. Brickman, Seven Seas, and their annual earnings numbers were getting squeezed squarely in the middle. It was a ritual struggle every season, with buyers working in concert against him, while the Alaskan packers were in a street rumble, at each other's throats, and unable to agree on even the simplest defensive strategy against the Japanese. The buyers would frequently employ an aggravating strategy of attrition by playing one packer against the other, stringing them both along. Maddening cycles of engagement, delay, and postponing their purchase agreements until the season were already underway, and selling options were dwindling to none. By the time the Japanese agreed to sign orders, the producers were so desperate for needed cash that they would cave in to nearly any concession just to get a deal done. They often wound up working for little or no margin, just to wrest some semblance of a season from the disaster.

Brickman detested the role of "the monkey in the middle" game, and he was determined that year that he would change the game for good. He hatched a plan that included buying national ad space for an exclusive king-crab retail promotion with Newday Stores, and he planned to break it in print and television at the peak of Japan's buying season. He had written Newday a personal guarantee that Seven Seas would compensate Newday for the costs of the promo if Seven Seas was unable — because of unforeseen "seasonal availability issues" — to deliver the crab sold by the ads. At the same time, he ordered promotional advertising copy mocked up that contained the logos of every major grocery store chain in the U.S., and had copies of the ads spread liberally around the office, including on his own desk. Word soon spread about the massive crab promotion being planned by Seven Seas. News of it even reached many of the industry's trade publications. A day prior to his meeting with Daichi Umi, Brickman had ordered the Seven Seas' company carpenter up to his office. The man had never met Brickman, much less been in his office, and as he entered the room, Brickman closed the door behind him. His instructions were simple. The carpenter was to saw Brickman's desk in two on a center line from the front to the back, but leave just enough surface veneer intact to provide minimal stability. The idea was for the desk to collapse under even a moderate downward force. The carpenter was sworn to secrecy and for his silence, Brickman would pay him $500 at the time and another $500 in a month, assuming that the story hadn't leaked in the meantime. After carefully completing the cut, the carpenter touched up the surfaces, then placed an light support piece below the cut to ensure that the desk would split simply by kicking out the support. Meanwhile, Brickman had purchased the heaviest, large-barreled, solid ash Louisville Slugger baseball bat he could find, and positioned it directly behind his desk, leaning it against the credenza where he kept market orders and agreements.

When the buyers arrived he made them wait in his office for nearly an hour. No drinks, and little to entertain themselves with but their own jet-lagged, semi-consciousness and a cabinet containing his handgun collection (brought in specifically for the event). To add to their anxiety, a vast confusion of multicolored king crab retail promotional artwork lay strewn across his desk, featuring giant banners that read "Buy One, Get One Free" and "Special Pearl Harbor Day Feature," On the right corner of his desk, aligned with his blood-red, brass-riveted leather humidor, was a matching stand with striker and safety matches, which, at its base, formed a leather tray perfectly sized for, and holding, a short stack of $100 bills. The bills, in turn, neatly faced a top-hinged, brass paper weight that appeared, at a distance, to be approximately the size, shape, and texture of a pair of human testicles.

Brickman entered the room from a side door that leads up an iron stairway from the receiving docks two floors below. He appeared to have not showered or shaved in more than a week, and he carried a pungent combination of body odor, stale cigars, and the ineffable stench of old fish. His clothes were as filthy as a deckhand coming off a two-week trip. As he fell into his chair, he wiped snot from his beard with his left hand, and in a single motion, flipped open the humidor and offered cigars to his guests, which they "orientally" declined. He promptly clipped a Don Diego Lonsdale for himself and, while spouting on about how happy he was that they had come to visit him, and with an enraptured audience watching in astonishment, he proceeded to ignite one, then another, and then a third $100 bill from the stack by the humidor, dropping each burning bill in turn into the ashtray. Oddly, the smoldering paper masked his stench with the never-to-be-forgotten odor of cremating Ben Franklins.

"They taste a lot better this way!" he declared as he reached for a bottle of 18-year-old, single-barrel Cartavio rum, and the four glasses that were parked in the large drawer below the telephone.

"Well gents, let's drink up!"

His five visitors were from the king crab section of Daichi Umi, including the director and his number two. Brickman had come to refer to the pair affectionately as "Cheech and Chong," and they had been a interminable thorn in his ass since Daichi Umi had hired the Japanese pair fresh from Harvard Business School to negotiate their Alaskan fisheries contracts. But this time would be different. Brickman had instructed his assistant to be sure that there was one fewer seat available in his office than the number of visitors. Once they were delivered to his office, an ad hoc game of musical chairs had ensued until Cheech dispatched the junior-most member of the team back to the lobby to busy himself browsing a collection of vintage SEVENTEEN magazines that Brickman had ordered to replace the lobby's standard fare of trade magazines and fishing gazettes.

These tough-headed veterans of the king crab wars with Seven Seas had experienced Brickman in every hue of rage over price, but this time he had clearly planned something altogether different. Just minutes into the meeting they were already visibly shaken by his absurd performance. And knowing his tendency to escalate any proceedings that didn't go his way, they sat guarded and smiling as Brickman proceeded to fog the room with the giant burner glowing between his teeth. His piercing eyes stared at them silently through the haze, doing a respectable squint-eye imitation of William Munny in THE UNFORGIVEN. The two rookie players, who were brought along to observe, now sat riveted to their chairs, captured in a textbook "shit-or-go-blind" moment, thinking that if only they had lost at musical chairs just moments before they would have been banished to the safety of the lobby. They, too, could be, at this moment, blissfully thumbing through photo galleries of post-pubescent girls in make-up ads.

Brickman brought the neck of the rum bottle to his mouth and yanked the cork out with his teeth. There was a sudden fumbling in the custom linen shirt pockets and fine silk slacks for cigarettes and gold-plated lighters. After serving himself, Brickman poured the rum into the thick, crystal tumblers and began serving them across the desk, in reverse order of seniority. When he reached for the fourth tumbler he suddenly hesitated, held the glass up to the light, then looked up with a smile and began polishing the lip of the glass on the soiled sleeve of his flannel shirt. He then filled the glass with the rich amber liquid and slid it across the desk to "Chong," who could see, even from his seated view point just below the plane of the desk top, that Brickman had failed in his feeble attempt to erase from the edge of the tumbler the multiple Cherry Red Maybelline lip prints. The lipstick suggested that another, more intimate, conversation had recently occurred in this same office, and Brickman wanted to make sure they knew about it.

By the third round — Brickman was on his fifth — the conversation had moved to pricing and the agreement. Cheech initiated the ritual "dance" about it being too early in the season to price the crab, and how the quota wasn't finalized yet, and his uncertainty regarding crab demand in Japan this year with the economic slowdown, and that it would be best to wait until later in the season before they could make any commitments about price and quantity. Chong added his requisite bad method acting by rocking his low-slung head slowly left to right, while punctuating each of Cheech's concerns with a rummied-up, but distinctly Japanese, grunt of agreement.

That was precisely the moment Brickman had been waiting for. As he rose from his chair, both the men leaned back slowly into theirs. Brickman turned and picked up the closed red folder on the top of his credenza. He opened it slowly and removed a paper-clipped set of documents on Seven Seas letterhead. He placed the papers carefully in front of them.

"Here are my terms." He then proceeded to outline his price and his delivery schedule for the coming season, gesturing broadly with the tumbler, and spilling the contents across the desk. The Daichi Umi team began to squirm nervously in their seats, as if suddenly struck down with a synchronous attack of the piles. Visibly agitated, Cheech began the classic, "We-are-so-very-sorry, Mr.-Brickman" defense, feigning a dismissive lack of interest in discussing the agreement, then smiling and pushing the document gently back across the desk. But the anxiety created by Brickman's antics had weakened Cheech's resolve, and had put him off his game. He was unable to muster the necessary arrogance to offer the more insulting coup de grace, ". . . but we must leave now for another appointment." He would soon wish he had. His tactical plan wilted as his growing apprehension about the negatives were piling up against him. All the while, his malevolence for Brickman's intimidating role play was growing.

Brickman continued, "I've covered the important stuff. We both know that these are reasonable numbers. I'm not gonna lose money on king crab so that you folks can come back here and buy California real estate. Sign it now or it's over."

"But Mr. Brickman, we are, of course, honored by your offer to sell us your fine product. Naturally, the reputation of Seven Seas is esteemed in Japan. But unfortunately, we cannot . . ."

At that, Brickman reached behind himself, grabbed the Louisville Slugger with his right hand, and began slapping the barrel of the bat slowly against the palm of his left.

"Sign it now, or get out!" His voice was now forceful and uncompromising.

"But Mr. Brickman . . ."

Brickman raised the bat above his head until it scuffed the ceiling tiles, and with one grand motion slammed the barrel down flatly against the center of the desk exactly above the cut. Simultaneously he kicked out the invisible support. The $3,000 oak desk split and collapsed, along with $2,000 in crystal tumblers, fine 100-proof Trinidad rum, and a shower of Ben Franklins. The stunned Cheech and Chong launched backwards out of their chairs, and, while grabbing for their briefcases, stumbled toward the door. Ill prepared, their attendants, sitting behind them, had been slow to move and now all four were trapped, pell-mell, at the doorway as Brickman rounded the desk carrying the bat and screaming like a madman that he was going to . . . give the crab away to fucking Newday before I will sell them another pound!"

Daichi Umi signed the agreement that season, and though there was a minor concession on the logistical arrangements, it was otherwise unaltered from the form Brickman had presented. From that day forward the buyers were especially cautious when entering into negotiations with Seven Seas, much less Ryan Brickman.

Each year, he came up with a new mind-bending tactic to throw them off their game. One year he had everyone in his office wear red T-shirts emblazoned with "Slap A Jap" across the front and "Remember Pearl Harbor" across the back. "I want to give them cause to pause before requesting any concessions from the undisputed king of Alaskan king crab."

. . . .

"Ryan, I feel that the plan you are about to present to us is dangerous, having many risks for Daichi Umi and for me personally."

Mika Vargas, the translator, is wearing an amber and gold embroidered, high-neck silk jacket. The pink jade bangle on her wrist is matched to the circular pendant suspended on a rope of 24-carat gold beads around her neck. Her hair is turned up with lacquered pins, creating a perfect circle of double-black silk framing the natural melancholy beauty of her flawless Andean-Oriental features. As she speaks, Watanabe turns slightly to his left so that he is eye-to-eye with Brickman. His visage is solemnity at attention, like a surgeon about to make an initial incision when the outcome has an equal probability of life and death. Though his words describe concern, there is no appearance of worry in his face. Maruhan once observed that "He can speak comfortably of his own mortality," as if his experiences have put him at ease in dealing with even the greatest uncertainty, even with death itself. He seems to have learned to be perfectly at ease with the present

— a master at conforming comfortably to his responsibilities in the moment.

"We call it Budo," Maruhan said, the warrior stance. One who is fearless of any outcome, to death itself."

Brickman responds, "Hak has explained to you exactly what my concerns are for the coming season. I hope he has made it clear that my management team and business associates are looking for my guidance. They, too, are tired of losing money to the retailers in Japan, as they play all vendors against each other for their price points. Akiro, I understand that my plan may not be acceptable to you and your colleagues. I can think of a number of reasons that you might not want to take this risk, and I'm sure that you have other reasons that I have not even considered. Hak has told me that you are personally responsible for the marketing decisions for Japan's big-three seafood houses, and also that as CEO of Daichi Umi, there is much pressure on you from the politicians to find ways to bring prices down. They want you to help appease Japanese consumers with lower costs on seafood products, which is so critical to the mood in the economy. I also understand that you, like me, are receiving much pressure from the large customers to lower prices. They are threatening you now with direct offers from the Russians and from the other new players, like this fellow Kiki, who is rumored to be buying in Alaska with the help of the Yakuza."

"Yes, these men were once working with us, but when the economy turned down, they began 'eating from our plate,' and now they are becoming very aggressive. Much of their business is in cash dollars, which they have trouble converting to bank funds.

They've learned that they can pay for the crab in cash in Alaska, and so they carry money into Dutch Harbor by the suitcase full to buy directly, using floating processors in the bay before exporting the crab to Japan for direct sale to retailers. Even if they are losing money they don't care, just so they can safely convert the cash into clean bank deposits."

"Akiro, there are too many crab buyers in the market. Right now in America every store is buying king crab. In Europe, also. The price is too high. The price cycle is overbought, and my people predict a fall in the market. It will drop by 50 percent of its current value over the next six months before it stops. The only question is when it will happen? Can you answer that for me?"

Brickman pauses, but before Vargas completes the translation he continues. "I will not lose millions of dollars waiting for the market to drop. Perhaps you also share in my frustration?"

Now he pauses again, looking for any acknowledgement in Watanabe's eyes as Vargas translates.

Then he continues, "I suggest that together we can bring the collapse now, when it is safe to do so because we are in control of the outcome. Otherwise, it will certainly happen anyway, but it will be out of our control, and there will be chaos in the market. We will both lose a lot of money."

Watanabe leans slightly forward in the chair. His upper body is rocking almost imperceptibly from front to back as Brickman continues.

"The idea, Akiro, is to bring the global market for king crab down now by shorting the market. Perhaps you can do this alone, but I cannot. I need your help."

Watanabe's deep graveled voice breaks in, but still barely above a whisper. Though he speaks little Japanese, Brickman has become a student of voice tone and has noted that with Asian languages in particular, the ending vowels often become extended and rise or fall as business conversations draw either closer to agreement, or closer to termination. He believes that Watanabe is following him.

Vargas listens to Watanabe intently, then nods, and turns back to Brickman.

"Daichi controls nearly one third of the global supplies, and we are capable of driving this market on our own. We are aware that the market is vulnerable, and when we feel it is the right time, then we can stop buying. We will move the market as we wish."

His statement is merely an illusion of strength, and both men know it. Brickman perceives it as another positive sign. He has the feeling that Watanabe is signaling his intent to support the plan, but on his terms. To make it happen, Brickman must build a "golden bridge" for Watanabe to cross honorably. He must present the details in a way that creates the sense that this is a shared strategy, inspired from the beginning by his respect for Daichi Umi and Watanabe. Fish is important to the Japanese, and here is the "Fish King" in the flesh about to lend his weight to a plan that could yield millions in profit. Brickman knows he must sell Watanabe back his dream of controlling the market, but from a position of strength, not of concession, by offering the considerable weapons at his command to make Watanabe's outcome a reality.

Again, Watanabe speaks, his voice louder and more emphatic than before, suddenly diving a full octave to a slow rumbling growl. Vargas translates: "Why should we work with you, Mr. Brickman? You have caused us much difficulty in the past. If the head of my crab section knew I was meeting with you now he would be very concerned, very embarrassed. He does not trust you."

Brickman has feared that his previous antics with Cheech and Chong might come back to haunt him, but he had never seriously considered the psychic shock — the *katanashi* — that Daichi's executives might suffer at the hands of his wanton negotiations with them. His mind races through myriad responses to defend his prior behavior, while protecting his ego, and his sense of righteousness. But then the thought occurs to him: Do I want to be right, or do I want to win? Is the point of this trip to demonstrate my superior tactical skill in negotiations, or is it to create an ally who will earn me tens of millions of dollars over the next 100 days?

"Akiro, you are correct. I have battled many times with your people over the price of crab and salmon. It is a battle that we will, no doubt, continue to fight for many years to come. And I have used every trick I know to win, because I believe, as you do, that winning is the only acceptable outcome. Am I sorry that I offended them? Well, perhaps I am. But I make no apologies for the past, and no promises that I will change my ways with Daichi Umi in the future. Because I am not a stockholder, I have no particular business concern with the well-being of Daichi, one way or another. I have only my own self-interest, and that of the Seven Seas Company, as my motive. I can only achieve this plan with your participation and your confidence. But your words suggest to me that, on balance, there is more weight discouraging this trust than inspiring it. There are more reasons for 'No' than for 'Yes.' So with that in mind, I have just one more question."

Brickman pauses to allow the room to prepare for the gravity of what he is about to ask. He has learned from Watanabe the power of holding the moment in mid-air, of not letting it land just yet, of allowing it to steep like tea in a pot until it has reached just the right temperature and color and flavor to be easily and eagerly swallowed.

"Tell me, Akiro, is our conversation over?"

The room falls silent, except for the hissing of the wind through the zebra grass beyond the terrace. There's also the chiming of white porcelain and silver as a red-lacquered bamboo tray is delivered to the center of the table, and cups are distributed and tea poured.

Watanabe begins talking, and as he does, he surprisingly pronounces one term in English: "1976." Vargas explains that 1976 was the last year that the Japanese fleet had open fishing rights for king crab in Alaska. Eight years later, the market collapsed, preceded by a short-catch-driven 60 percent market climb before finally capitulating under its own weight. A dozen years later, the U.S. government imposed a conservation plan for king crab, triggering another market boom that similarly busted in its 13th year, causing widespread market losses in Japan and the U.S. Thin production in 1995 resulted in a similar market fall in 1996.

Watanabe continues, "Eight, 13, and 21 belong to a mathematical set of predictive numbers that our analysts have used for many years to reliably predict the outcomes of commodity markets. They tell me that this year is also such a Fibonacci year, and, as you have said, the particular conditions of over speculation going onto this season will create a particularly dangerous market decline. So, Mr. Brickman, I suggest that we have quite a number of things to discuss. I would say that our conversation is not yet over. In fact, it is just beginning."

As Maruhan drives him back to the airport, Brickman reviews the reverse time line that he and Watanabe have constructed for the execution of their plan. He also looks at the arithmetic of what he will need in working capital to make the plan work.

"Christ, did I really just commit to a $150 million short?"

Timing for the cash will depend on when, exactly, they will begin accelerating the bidding for crab, and then the pacing of the revised price targets they plan to broadcast to the marketplace. They have coordinated logistical delays that are designed to slow deliveries and back up stocks, which will also control the cash flow. When the market is ripe, Brickman will order the upward revision in the U.S. Cold Storage Holdings report, a trigger sign for companies to begin dumping product. They will forward offers into the marketplace on all three continents, and that will precipitate the crash. But the big money will be needed afterwards. They have already agreed on the safe price level when they will step back into the market and begin buying all the stock they can. They will coordinate the buying so that they aren't bidding against each other for the same crab stocks. Of the ¥200 billion total production, they plan to erase $1 billion U.S. dollars worth of market value in less than two weeks. That will be nearly 50 percent. If all goes according to plan, bedsides the thousands of small players speculating on king crab, the number-one bag holder will be none other than "Stalin," followed closely by "Machine Gun Kiki" of the Yakuza.

Brickman licks his upper lip and turns his head, focusing deep out to the horizon where a tropical depression has formed an H-bomb-sized monsoon shaft in an otherwise flawless sky. He punches the "Favorites" button on his iPhone.

CHAPTER 22

Jane's mobile phone is vibrating as she struggles in vain with the magnetic key to get into her room the Hotel Metropolitan. "Room 8500, right?," she says to no one. The instructions on the card are in Flemish, French, and Italian, and after rotating through all four permutations twice, she gives up, drops her bag and takes her phone out of her pocket.

"Hold on, I'm almost there." She grabs her Bluetooth earpiece from her bag, which she hikes over her shoulder, and begins dragging her roller bag back down the hall toward the elevator. Brickman hears the tone of the elevator bell in the background as Jane fiddles with her earpiece.

"What's that? Are you still on the plane? Aren't you in Brussels yet? Hell, you need to do the presentation in the morning. What's going on?"

"Damn card keys. Can you hear me? Remember, I took the train from Paris. I'm sorry, Ryan, I'm in the conference hotel, but it's a mess. The place is under construction, and I'm nervous as hell about the presentation. I'm meeting Og in an hour, and I can't even get into my room. By the way, are you back in San Francisco?"

"I'm at Kahului. I'm sorry about your room, Kid. You know those block-heads are used to living in fishing boats. They don't know any better. Listen Jane, the outcome of your presentation is important to me. Do you understand? We'll talk about the reasons why when we meet in Denver on Wednesday, but the stakes are much higher now. I need your "A Game." If you pull this off, you're a hero."

"Ryan, I don't want to be a hero. Heroes get slaughtered. This is not what I do. I'm in sales, not finance. I've already learned that lesson."

There's a pause as Jane arrives at the front desk and complains about the key and the condition of the hallway to her room, which is filled with scaffolds and paint buckets. She insists on being moved to a new room. They change her key to one for a recently refurbished room in a completed hallway, and she is on her way back up, this time to room 8560.

"Jane, don't let these guys get out the door without a decision. I want a stake in the ground on this financing. Once you've fixed a date and time for the next action, you will have started their bankers 'RAM' running the calculus on how to get the deal done. If they resist making a commitment, don't be afraid to question their intentions. Ask them if it's over. They'll panic. Everyone comes to them begging for money. Be just the opposite. I want you to sound like we are qualifying them to be our banker, not vice versa."

"But wait a minute, Ryan. You're talking about at the end of the presentation aren't you? After I've spoken about the company and what we do, correct?"

"Sure, the decision is at the end. But you're going to be laying the ground work throughout the whole talk. I never want you to give them the sense that you are trying to impress them. None of that 'We're the biggest' horse shit. Do you understand?"

"But Ryan, the whole PowerPoint is about . . . us!"

"Dump it!

"What!?"

"Forget the PowerPoint, Jane. You don't need it. Trust me. They are salivating over the Hoffman business already, and they know that you are the one who put it together. You're the 'rainmaker.' If bankers were any good at selling, they wouldn't be stuck peddling cash at 2.5 percent gross profit. Bankers are always mystified by successful sales people because they've seen so many great businesses fail because they don't have one. Sales systems are the bottleneck in many good companies, and it ends up choking them to death. To a banker, a great sales system and a strong customer base are the iron-clad backstop for any risk in extending a large credit line. So they are dazzled by sales authority. And you're the best at it. The bigger the money, the more it matters, and I'm looking for a hundred million, Kid."

"OK, no pressure, right! Now about the PowerPoint thing. I'll tell you, Ryan, unless Og manages to get these guys talking business, it's going to be a very short presentation without it. There are limits to how long I can keep them entertained with beauty and charm alone."

"They're going to love you, Jane. Trust me. You will charm them, and it will make them more certain they are with the right people. The more certainty you can create around our sales process, the more they'll want the deal. They need to move money like we need to move fish. Bankers are like anybody else: It's a matter of perception. Their world is about risk, and they are starving for anything that will galvanize certainty in a deal — any numerical proof that removes risk. You get it? Insisting on dates and times for the next steps communicates to them that you are a low-risk businessperson. That you are a 'decisioner.'"

"Ryan, I get what you're saying. Even without the PowerPoint, I can ad-lib forever about Seven Seas and our mix of terrific customers. I can nail them down on a time line. No problem. But the message I get from Og is this: To get the deal we want, we'll need to do more. They respect control and strength. If our approach is solicitous, we may as well stay home. We need to challenge Islandbanc to explain why they think our deal won't work. Asking them 'Why not?' rather than telling them 'Why not.' I've had a couple of experiences on this trip that are changing my thinking when it comes to how we approach any deal. I'm calling it 'anti-sales.' It's not about us, Seven Seas. It's about the prospect, and what they want to accomplish. The outcome they are looking to achieve with Seven Seas. If we make assumptions about what's going on in their heads, we're toast. So, before we press them, I want them to give up the truth. I'm going to find out what's beneath the surface that threatens to wreck this deal months down the road — just about the time we've convinced ourselves that it's all smooth sailing ahead. If there's an iceberg out there, I agree with Og. Let's find out about it tomorrow morning."

"Listen Jane, honestly, I don't care how you do it. You're the genius in guiding clients to a decision. That's all I'm asking you to do. Once you have them nailed down on the next step, I know the rest of this will fall into place. What I don't want is to let it slide. Hell, you are better off with a 'No' than you are with a 'Let us think about it and get back to you sometime.' Find out what it takes to get the next action step from them, a date and time. I don't care what it is. Just make sure you get an appointment for the next event in the process. Remember, you can't kill a good deal, but you can delay it to death."

"Ryan, you know my problem is trying to not kill the foot dragging prospects! Honestly, I wish I had more patience with them, but when they start spinning my wheels, I just feel the need terminate them. I'll be more patient with bankers though. I promise!"

"One more thing, Jane. If you get a chance, role play some Q and A with Og. He's an Icelander. He runs in the same circles as these fellows. Let him guide you on what they might be thinking, and what they will ask. But just remember, this is your meeting. Og's just an advisor. So, run it the way you see fit. Go get 'em, Killer!"

CHAPTER 23

Jane is excited about the dinner with Og Johannson and Magnus Krisuvik, CEO of Islandbanc. And after sharing some light moments about the problems they are all encountering with the construction at the hotel, the conversation quickly changes to business. Jane's opening remarks suggest that even though working capital is not an important issue for Seven Seas at present, the company's strategic plan keeps them continuously in the hunt for more favorable banking arrangements. Thin commodity margins make the interest rate an important part of profitability. Her responsibility at tomorrow's talk is to help the bank understand the customer side of the Seven Seas business, and, in turn, for her to learn something about what the bank is ideally seeking from new clients.

Krisuvik opens with a candid talk about some of the business development issues at the bank related to changes in their capital growth. He talks about how they had recently expanded their international service offerings, and are eager to put those changes to work.

Jane dissects each of his comments, looking for the threads of his core motivations for being here. She asks questions that clarify,

simplify, and test the significance of any of his words that suggest
a comment is emotionally rooted in a deeper personal context.
These are her reality-testing questions, and they are helping her
understand exactly what makes the Seven Seas deal important to
Krisuvik himself, and to his colleagues on the loan committee. She
wants a clear picture of what the perfect outcome means to him,
and to challenge whether or not it makes sense to him for Seven
Seas to be included in the picture. He discusses the issues they
are having with U.S. dollar inflows, some of the mistakes they've
made in deploying those funds, and the fact that they are now
seeking solid, ongoing transactional accounts that can use medium
nine-figure, dollar-asset-based lines of credit. He defers to one of
his vice presidents to cover a check list of other services they are
looking to bill: Letter of Credit negotiations, foreign exchange
hedging, etc. But most important, the bank is seeking a client
that requires a trusted banking partner with established business
connections in the new Russian Federation.

Besides the obvious dovetailing with the credit facility and the
other international services the bank offered, the business with
"Stalin" and the Russian king crab program (with the inherent
shipping through Saigon for processing, etc.), has become a
documentation nightmare. If Islandbanc's Russian organization
can streamline the process, the relationship will be just little
short of perfect. But Jane deliberately withholds any statements
that acknowledge that this complement has already become
compellingly clear. Instead, she allows Krisuvik to continue
answering her questions around the fit, rather than trying to make
assertions that, at this point, could sound like she is reaching for
the deal.

Jane loathes the impression that results when a salesperson jumps in with both feet as soon as a prospect mentions the need for some product or service, especially in an initial sales conversation. It always sounds phony to her. Even if the claim is genuine it instantly draws suspicion. Any assertion made in the context of a sales conversation is automatically interpreted by the prospect as false. Unless there is a powerful basis of trust between the parties, an assertion — even with "evidence" — is a red flag to a buyer. A salesperson's over-zealous response to a prospect's need — "Oh yeah, we do that!" — almost always triggers an automatic response in the prospects mind: "No, you don't do that! You are just saying that to try to sell me. I know that because my brain hasn't decided to wire you into my 'trust' matrix yet, so I don't know yet if you are planning to help me or harm me. And, in fact, your assertion is suggesting the latter. So, just to prove that you aren't qualified to sell me that thing that I just told you I need, I'm going to turn right around and hire your competitor instead!"

Jane has convinced herself that the best way to inform a prospect is to reveal her knowledge and fit through the questions she asks them, not by telling them, or trying to be the smartest person in the room. It just doesn't work when what you claim as true is ignored or worse, rejected as false.

The dinner ends with Og Johannson's observation that a breakfast meeting, combined with jet-lag, suggests an early end to this dinner. Returning to her room, Jane turns off the lights, opens the sliding door to the balcony, and walks to the railing with her after-dinner 777 cigarette glowing between her fingers, like the tail lights of the cars streaming between the trees that line Place de Brouckere, eight floors below.

"What the hell makes deals close?" she says out loud. It's a question that has circulated in her random access memory for as long as she can remember. She has spent her career thinking that it's her skill and technique, her particular tenacity, or personality, and her ability to build relationships with her clients. But the truth is, she is not particularly adept at any one of those tasks. She knows plenty of folks who are more skilled than she is at selling, but haven't gotten nearly as far as she has in building a book of business. So what is the truth? She is beginning to formulate a new way of seeing deal-making as work that is more predetermined, more dependent on the prospect, and not what she is looking to achieve. Her role is little more than engaging the decision-maker in a conversation in which she, Jane, acts as the decision-taker. If the prospect has an actionable outcome that she can make real, then her job is simply to guide them through the decisions and get it done. That is all. But the outcome has to be in their heads to begin with, because people don't decide to take action on anything unless they have created — or been assisted in creating — a three-dimensional picture in their own heads of the ideal outcome of an important issue or aspiration. It's a simple, yet profound, truth: People who have no pictures of imaginary futures cannot aspire to them. Remarkable achievers have the talent to create detailed future realities in their minds, coupled with the tenacity to nurture the picture, to grow it, and to build on it with granular detail until it becomes reality.

"Don't be the frog in the well." Jane's taekwondo instructor once gave her an ancient Zen Buddhist exercise to help her develop the skill for controlling her perceptions of time and sequence when engaged in a sparring match.

"Imagine you are The Creator," he told her. "You are creating the fight in its entirety, including your opponent and his actions, so you can ultimately control it."

In a state of meditation, the instructor had encouraged her to imagine that she is actually the source of all of the reality that she experiences. She should imagine that there is really no one else in the universe — no other entity or source of energy exists external to her own creative consciousness. Everything she experiences is a result of her own creation — every human being she encounters; every blooming flower she sees, touches, and smells; every ticking moment of the clock. She should see all of it as a fabrication of her own mind and imagination.

"Your body is doing a thousand things right now that your mind is not consciously controlling, and you are not consciously aware of. Your breathing, it is automatic. So it is with your opponent's attack. He is like your breath. His every action is a surprise to you until you become aware of it. Then you seize control. But to take it, you must gain release from your fear of control."

He taught her to release her thinking into the vastness of the concept. She recalls the remarkable sense of power, freedom, and dread solitude it conveys — the warmth that floods through her body. She played with the notion that even the movement of the moon across the sky was her creation, pretending that she alone was the source and cause of everything she saw and touched and felt about the world around her, and that she'd been assembling the universe all along and was just now awakening to human realization of it.

"And now the final step," he had said. She sat in silence, suspended in the present with just his voice. "Now imagine that what I've told you is real. Even my voice that you are hearing now is your own creation. There is really no me. There is no Sensei. Only you. You are The Master. You have brought to yourself in this moment the full awareness of you. You are the God you have longed for, and pondered about, and only you have the power to create reality from your own vision of the outcome."

The result of the meditation exercise on her sparring was remarkable. She began seeing her opponents moves in decelerated time, reading their body language that telegraphed a punch or a kick seemingly several seconds before they actually occurred. That gave her valuable time to prepare the perfect response. Her achievements on the sparring mat soared. It was as if her opponent had become her partner in her victories.

Through these "Creator" meditations, two important dots had been connected in Jane's mind. First, for all practical purposes, there is no productive alternative to thinking of reality other than the future we choose to create — bending the universe to our will by investing ourselves totally in the future as we already see it in our mind's eye. Second, because our accomplishments are mainly in conjunction with other people, we need to understand precisely what outcomes other people want to achieve if we are to enable our own. In business, we must learn to reveal the intentions and outcomes of the prospect — to read and understand the messages they telegraph to us about what they are truly thinking and aspiring to if we are to manifest the business that we depend upon them to help us to create it.

CHAPTER 24

Jane is in the back of a morning taxi to Islandbanc's Brussels office at the Grand Place when she receives a call from David Shepard. He has just completed his presentation to his insurance client's Bern committee, which is deciding whether to include his "Expectation and Relationship" training as a permanent part of the risk-mitigation curriculum that they provide for surgeons and surgical personnel for whom they provide malpractice coverage.

"Jane, I got your call this morning. Listen, I'm at the airport, so I may break off at any time, I'm headed to my flight back to London. Are you in the cab to your presentation yet?" But before she can answer, "Remember, you are in control now. You own the room. You've prepared the stages using the e-mail I sent you yesterday, right?"

Jane eyeballs the sheet of paper which, in her nervousness, she's wadded up in her fist. She had printed out the e-mail at the hotel's Business Center on the way to her room after dinner last night. As usual, there were the requisite issues of getting logged into e-mail, then getting the printer to format the table on a single page. Though she was tired, she had scrawled what she could remember from her dinner with Og Johannson and Magnus Krisuvik into a list of bullets, and then drawn arrows to the stage that applied. She casts her eyes skyward and takes a deep breath. "Yep, I've got it."

"OK, It's 'Lights! Camera! Action' time. Once you begin with your prepared opening, your brain will kick in and you'll be on automatic pilot. That's fine. Just stay present and with them the whole time. If one of them so much as scratches his nose, make a mental note of it. No soliloquies. Keep it interactive."

"Got it. Present and observant and interactive."

"This is the confirmation step, Jane. You are going to play back to them the outcome that they've already told you they are looking for. In this Jane Dreyfus version, your power is in the process. Stick with it. Let the 'No Guessing Law' guide your questions past any assumptions you want to make. Remember, they want to write this agreement, or you wouldn't be there. So be explicit about getting the deal done. That's the only real purpose of the meeting."

"I'm present, ears and eyes wide open. I take command of the room. Nothing can block this deal that I can't tackle. I can ask any question that moves us forward to a decision, ultimately getting my outcome by focusing on theirs, right? I'm absolutely clear on that. OK, we are turning off . . ." Jane speaks to the cabbie, "*Cette est Rue Le Loi?*" Then back into the phone, "David, their office is just up the street now."

"Listen Jane, you sound a bit bothered. You're nervous, right? OK, I want you to do something for me that may sound a bit odd, but I promise, it will help you."

"OK, whatever you say."

"I want to yell, very loud, right now: Yes - I - Can!"

"Huh?"

"Yes - I - Can! It's from Teddy Roosevelt. So say it with every certainty."

"David, I'm in a cab."

"Doesn't matter, Mate. Let 'er rip. Come on, you promised me."

"Yes I can."

"Whad du' say, Mate?"

"Yes I Can. Yes I Can!"

"Emphasis on the CAN. Yes I CAN! got it?"

"YES I CAN!"

"Now let's hear it New Zealand style, Mate. Loud as you can, from the 'Cape to the Bluff!'"

As Jane's white LTI hackney cruises past the 15th century guild halls along Rue de La Loi, she is screaming the affirmation from the passenger compartment, much to the shock and dismay of the driver, who is barely protected by the safety pane between them.

"Seriously, Jane, every time I'm about to do a presentation, I find a spot off by itself where I can ground myself. I tear off with those three words, in three repetitions, from right down deep in me gut. When I do, my attitude changes, and I swear people take notice straight away. Whatever it is, it's contagious. If you start lagging, excuse yourself and do it again. Reset that intensity with another 'Yes I Can!'"

"Right. Thank God we're here."

The cab pulls up to the bronze plaque bearing three diagonal right-to-left stripes in relief, glazed blue-red-blue in enamel.

"David, one last thing. I appreciate the help, I do, and I'm, well . . . we need to talk about how this coaching thing works. I want to hire you. No time now, but let's figure it out."

"Listen Jane, I'm not certain there's a fit, us working together. There's a conversation we need to have about . . ."

"Not a fit. Right. I know, I know. We need to talk about the outcome I am looking to achieve, right?"

There's an audible chuckle from Shepard, overlaying the airport gate agent's announcement in the background.

"Right, Mate. Well, that's part of it. Tell you what, give me a call one week from today and we'll see if we talk about it. Deal?"

"Deal."

"Aces! OK, that's me plane, Jane. Have a ripper. Ta for now!"

After, fumbling through her few remaining Euros, Jane swings her legs to the right and springs from the cab, elevated by her conversation with Shepard. She has a powerful sensation that the meeting is already done and won, but she immediately admonishes herself for the luxury. Still, she is of a mind that there's nothing they can throw at her that she hasn't heard before. There's no need for pretense. She's free to focus on the real stuff: the answers that will get money on the move. There's no need to bother with the standard "window dressing" that she would typically waste time on in previous presentations.

She is led past a red leather couch and down a hallway of deep blue carpeting, flanked on the sides by white tile. There are large brushed steel frames adorning the teak walls, bearing black and white photos of geothermal plants, pharmaceutical laboratories, fishing boat construction, and various other scenes of commercial conquest that the bank's capital has enabled. In the conference room, on the top of the credenza is a tombstone display of various funding's involving the bank. Jane notices the unusually high number in commodity businesses, especially in the fishing and marine industries. Several are written in Cyrillic, and they contain some of the largest strings of zeros. "Russian," she thinks to herself. While scanning the meaningless letters, her eyes suddenly lock onto one string of characters she has seen before, and she translates them immediately. Repeated on three large tombstones is the term "**РЕД ЦРАБ,**" "Red Crab."

A curious coincidence, Jane thinks. Seven Seas' business with the Russians isn't a secret. Certainly there is a fair chance that Magnus

Krisuvik is aware of it. But why didn't it come up over dinner last evening when they were all discussing the bank's operations in the Russian Republic. Is it pure coincidence that Og Johannson referred Ryan Brickman to Islandbanc within weeks of initiating the huge Russian crab deal, particularly with processing through communist Vietnam? The Icelanders have a niche in dealing with the Russians — and probably a very profitable one, since few banks are prepared to handle the risks of trading in the "Wild Wild East." What could be the reason for the bank's wanting to have control on both sides of the trade in Russian crab — both the Russian sell side and the American buy side?

Krisuvik, Johannson, and three others enter the room, followed by an administrative assistant with a cart of coffee and pastries.

"You look as rested as if you'd slept in your own bed." Krisuvik greets her with a toothful smile and a warm grasp of her arm with both hands, pulling her gently towards the conference table. "Let me introduce you to the team."

Jane listens carefully to his entrées, quickly forming a mnemonic for the otherwise impossible Icelandic names, all the while looking each person squarely in the eye with her signature, genuine Duchenne smile. But her attention is drawn to the sole woman, a classic Nordic with the effortless appearance of a natural beauty, unencumbered by thin titanium spectacles and close cropped hair, which falls just above her shoulders.

"Jane, this is Hella Elgar. Hella is Islandbanc's new President of Eurasian commercial lending."

Her eyes are a glacial-transparent blue. The exchange of greetings has none of the artificial "friendliness" that is typical of male business introductions. Men usually react in one of two ways when confronted with Jane's dominant personality. They are either intimidated, or are veiled with sexual interest (what she calls the "professional eunuch": someone who seems to have completely subverted their own sexuality. In other words, business androgyny.) But not Elgar. Jane instantly feels her pulse. Her handshake is at ease, not forced, intentional, or manly. There is no hint of the affectation of position or authority. Her smile is ready, reserved, and sincere, beginning at the corners of her eyes and moving along a well-traveled path to the corners of her mouth. As Jane watches her, Elgar's head shifts gently to the right, and her chin slightly forward. Her smile transitions from a greeting to a hint of curiosity, and the widening of her eyes says that she is taking in the moment.

"Hella has just joined us from directing Lehman Brothers' Eastern European office in Moscow."

Introductions complete, Jane turns to the bank's CEO, "Magnus, I am ready to begin whenever you folks are." As everyone settles in, Jane checks the clock on the wall, and then turns back to the group.

"First, thank you for the invitation to come and speak with you about the prospects for a working relationship between Islandbanc and Seven Seas. I have planned our talk for about 40 minutes, but I have some extra time, if need be. We are an intimate group, so I'm hoping it will be as much a conversation as a presentation. Is everyone comfortable with that timing?"

With that, she removes her cell phone from her jacket pocket and switches it to silent mode before setting it down in front of her on the conference table.

"Before we begin, I would like to bring something important to your attention, and update you on the situation. You may already be aware that five days ago Seven Seas lost two of its new king crab fishing vessels in the Bering Sea, north of Dutch Harbor, along with a tragic loss of all hands, including the Karensen brothers, from Iceland."

The Icelanders appear remarkably restrained, almost indifferent to the announcement, except for Krisuvik, who speaks after a brief pause as if in sudden recognition of a propriety dictated by the moment.

"Yes, yes, we are naturally sad with the news of the disaster. The story has been in the press in Reykjavik, and I informed the others this morning on the information you had given me last evening."

Elgar follows quickly on Krisuvik's words, "Yes, we are saddened for the families of course, very much," and then with only a slight pause, which Jane can't tell is callousness or a simple lack of fluency with the language, she shifts the tone, "however, can you tell us if you see any material impact to the business coming from this unfortunate event?"

Though it strikes Jane as an odd transition, rather than cueing any awkwardness, she decides to soften her reply, and defer a complete answer. "I'm glad that you asked that, Hella. Yes, it will change our sourcing plan, but we believe that the effects will not be significant for reasons I will come back to a little later in the presentation. That is, if you don't mind." They nod in agreement, and Jane continues.

"The purpose of my visit is that Seven Seas is seeking a partnership with an international bank to provide a commercial line of credit of 100 million U.S. dollars, at Libor plus 1.25. We will use the funding in our king crab packing and distribution operations. This capital requirement is part of our overall growth plan, so it is a strategic priority. The outcome we are looking to achieve today is an agreement on a time line for a mutual decision about the credit facility. My process will start with an interactive review of our business operations, the structure, and the opportunities that we looking to capitalize and the challenges that we see ahead in the business."

Jane is dressed in fine-hand, blue serge. A thick, deep knot of wavy chestnut hair is drawn behind her ears, appointed with ruby studs that collect the thin morning sun and take on the color and brooding glow of fresh embers of steel. Her athletic hands are planted like goal posts beside her hips, with her hips resting on the front edge of the same Danish credenza, which is adorned with a field of deal tombstones. Her tone is relaxed, and she bears a confident smile that belies her anxiety about talking about the deal quantified precisely as Brickman had described it to her, only once by phone just hours before this very moment.

"We have many important issues to talk about, in particular I want to be sure we come back to the current global markets in crab. But first I want to reinforce that mine is an interactive presentation. Magnus shared some the banks views and concerns over our dinner . . .," then, casting a smile and a nod, ". . . and thank you again, Magnus, for adding Belgian fried potatoes with mayonnaise and wheat beer to my culinary repertoire."

As the grins around the table subside, and the room relaxes momentarily, she continues. "But before I assume too much about your individual questions, let's go around the table, if you don't mind, and please tell me something about your role, and what you would like to hear from me that will help you in making an informed decision."

Knowing that every business decision is ultimately personal, she is hoping that, in opening the floor to individual comments from the lending committee members, perhaps something will be said that will reveal the one or more hidden issues that could blow up the deal down the road if uncovered and left to chance to resolve.

Og Johannson begins reciting a bureaucratic sounding, boiler-plate response about economic development between the two countries. As he speaks, Jane's mind drifts back to the "**РЕД ЦРАБ**" insignia, which is now positioned like a prop to her hand, stage right.

Uncertainty is a banker's nightmare. And as Jane sees it, the uncertainty for a banker in the international crab trade today rested squarely on the inflated market price. She has opened with it because she isn't going allow them to be the first to question what is clearly the element of greatest uncertainty in their entire conversation.

Brickman had discussed with her his growing concern at the frenzied pace of seafood promotions, the natural market cycle, and the rising popularity of king crab owing to the media and reality TV exposure had caused the market to climb too much over the previous 18 months. Primary and secondary wholesalers are vaguely aware that the price level is unsustainable, but the market has turned into a feeding frenzy. Many late comers view the market strength as an opportunity to speculate, leading to a build up of "old season" stocks in the U.S. and Japan, and all this while we are going into the new production season. The Japanese don't report cold storage stocks publicly, but the U.S. does, and the numbers have been steadily climbing as the market has continued to rise. The market action wasn't lost on the Russians. It is no secret among top traders that the Russians have been accumulating heavy stocks of crab. But because there are no reliable inventory estimates in the Russian Federation. Even the magnitude of their position is unknown. "'Stalin,'" according to Brickman, "is a wicked combination of gambler, liar, and thief. But he can turn on all the charm of a coffin salesman when he needs to."

King crab is a government-controlled business in Russia, meaning that "Stalin" has a virtually unlimited, sovereign-backed line of credit. If he sandbags the accounts-receivable figures reported to the bank, he can run up inventories ahead of the season opening, when he can sell stocks at huge margins. He can personally pocket the speculative gains while liquidating the standard contract profits in his reports back to his bosses. After all, it's a long way from Moscow to Vladivostok.

But, what if the bank has figured it out? After all, that's what they do! At this stage, the true size of the market exposure in Russian inventories pledged to the bank could be many tens of millions of dollars. With the market overbought, the bank's risk of a loss due to an unhedged market collapse could be critical. This is a season where the risk of assets are degrading to a level below the loan-to-value ratio, and the mistake can have career implications for anyone responsible. Perhaps it already has. Hadn't Krisuvik introduced Hella Elgar as the new head of Eurasian commercial lending?

Jane surmises that Islandbanc needs Seven Seas. With Seven Seas as a customer they will control both the cash and the goods, "cradle to grave," throughout the lifetime of the transaction for Russia's largest single customer. And in case of a fall, they will know where the money is, and how to control the flow of it to minimize bank's risk. Documentary control will also provide them with access to accurate details on what the Russians were selling, who they're selling it to, and for what price. Islandbanc is lending to the Russians on the basis of inventory and receivables, and with that exposure they need certainty about the state of those assets at any given time.

The real reason Jane is here is becoming clear to her. She has followed the money and figured out that it's not about the four or five cents made on the interest-rate spread, or the ancillary services on the U.S. side. It's always been about controlling risk: protecting the bank's downside. Deals only happen because a prospect needs to make it happen. In this case, the bank is seeking insurance against a potentially catastrophic loss.

"My role is to make decisions based on the risks related to extending the credit," Elgar says as she casts her eyes upward from her legal pad. Jane now senses the deeper purpose of the meeting, and makes the decision to test her theory at the next opportunity in the conversation. Elgar continues, "I have two questions related to those risks. The first is about the commodity risks related to market conditions that, as you mentioned, appear extended at present. And the second is related to Seven Seas' Russian business, and the numbers you are expecting in the current season from the Russian side."

Jane takes a deep breath. The number one rule in trading is never to telegraph your position to anyone at anytime. It always comes back to haunt you. "We are comfortable with the current market (a bald-faced lie), and we expect the demand and apparent consumption to continue at the current levels."

She continues according to the agenda, while focusing mainly on the issues and the outcome that Krisuvik had highlighted at dinner last night, and the insights about the bank that Johannson had shared, including the interest in managing the Russian transactions. The interactions are positive, and the group is engaged. Jane is feeling good about the progress. But, glancing at Johannson, she suddenly recalls his warning about "going negative," and not succumbing to "happy ears." After summarizing the presentation affirmatively, the expression on Jane's face changes to mild concern, and her voice becomes soberingly realistic.

"I have a question for the group. Perhaps it will expedite matters in one way or the other. We have talked about the reasons why this business would work. But what interests me is why a loan agreement between our companies will not happen. I'd love to hear from you the reasons why this is a bad idea."

Stunned silence. They all look at Jane as if she had just stripped naked in front of them. No prospective customer has ever challenged them on why they wouldn't make a loan. They would be no more surprised than had she said, "Listen, I really I don't care how this turns out, but enough of the window dressing. Let's just cut to the nitty-gritty and get on to the decision."

Hella Elgar is the first to speak. "What about the accumulated stocks in your inventory and in the markets? Surely you have concerns about the orderly sale of high inventories."

Janes thinks: Now we're finally to the crux of why Elgar is here. She looks down to her right, admiring her azure Cole Haan crossed casually to the left. As a guarded smile grows across her face, she rises to her feet. She senses they are getting close, but knows that to answer Elgar's question too quickly or too cleverly would be rushing the art of the deal. Elgar could end up feeling short-changed by the answer, and Seven Seas would be worse off than before because it might send the message that Jane has only a shallow interest in the bank's concerns.

Earlier in her career, Jane often admonished herself for repeating the rookie mistake of speeding to answer a prospect's question without giving it full consideration, or without providing the time and deliberation that the moment demanded. What had come to her (only with trial and error) was a critical sensitivity to timing in client conversations. To get in sync with the natural pace and rhythm requires careful listening to the prospect, making sure to understand the true purpose behind the words. When she does it right, it means an express elevator to a decision, usually a positive one. In effect, she has learned to slow the conversation down sometimes to make the deal go faster. This is such a time. Instead of being quick and smart, she will be slow and deliberate. She now holds the thread of the bank's true motive in her grasp, and she needs to follow it carefully to the source.

"Forgive me, Hella, I'm not evading your question. But I need to better understand your thinking so I can respond with a satisfactory answer."

Elgar nods in agreement, and Jane continues.

"I may be mistaken, but I imagine that the ebb and flow of seasonal inventories is common among the customers of the bank, and that you regularly evaluate the risk of those stocks as standard practice. So, I'm curious why our inventory positions are of special concern to you at this time, especially in the context of my question about why an agreement between our companies might not make sense."

"Yes, you are correct. Market risk is a standard calculation that we should always be making . . ."

Jane notes to herself, she said "should." Was that a language/grammar mistake, or was Elgar telegraphing to Jane while reminding the group that they have been negligent, and that there has been a failure of due diligence that has left the bank dangerously exposed to a market hit on king crab.

Elgar continues, "It is not necessarily Seven Seas' inventories that concern us. But rather, the combined positional risk in the marketplace. We are now looking at the global inventories, combined with the relative price of the market, and we see some risk there. So I am asking your opinion, from the Seven Seas vantage point."

After pausing to process her reply, Jane raises her head and makes eye contact with Elgar, fixing a gaze deep into those glacier blues. Jane decides to take this issue to the mat. This conversation is over if the bank is too frightened of their own exposed position to make a decision. Johannson won't find any more investors eager to put money into Iceland if their leading bank is already choking on king crab!

"We have a number of seasonal fisheries in the Pacific Northwest, where producers must learn to speculate successfully on the future of the markets if they are going to survive and prosper. We have a saying about that requirement that goes, "If you want to eat like an elephant, you'd better learn to shit like an elephant.'"

The room falls quite momentary, before bursting into a gaggle of Icelandic translation and interpretation led by Johannson. Suddenly, Krisuvik begins to stifle his chuckle, then laughs again, pounding on the edge of the conference table, before breaking into a sea lion roar so animated that it drags the rest of the crowd along with him.

"I'm sorry to be so blunt, but inventories are only a risk when you don't know where, when, and at what price you are going to sell them. Any company that succeeds in Alaska has mastered the art of being a market maker in the commodities they sell. Companies don't last long in this business if they don't deal with the uncertainties around their inventory positions, and about whether they've hedged those positions."

Elgar restrains a grin as she recovers from the interlude. "So you are saying to us that you are confident that you, at Seven Seas, are elephants?"

Casting her eyes around to each member of the group, Jane pauses at Krisuvik before smiling and turning back to Elgar. "Well, I suppose I would first ask you which answer, 'Yes' or 'No,' gives us the outcome we want. Which one gets us the loan agreement with Islandbanc at the terms we've requested?"

Elgar is caught off guard, and, missing the implied humor in the question, responds as if it were intended in complete sincerity. "Jane, we are not in a position to give a decision on the agreement at this point. There are naturally a number of other questions we have to . . ."

Jane senses a critical opening in the conversation. One thing she loves about business is the efficiency imperative. There's seldom a good excuse for dragging a process out any longer than necessary. It is the heart and soul of good business to "cut to the chase" when the time is right, and this is that time. She makes the decision to ignore Elgar's statement and to ask an reality-testing question that could at once test her analysis of the Russian business while, at the same time, move the conversation forward to a decision. She gently interrupts Hella's reply.

"Forgive me Hella, but I imagine that even in banking it is about having the right customers. If you're going to take in money, you had better know where to sell the money with as little risk as possible of losing it, yes? Otherwise, the depositors will simply go elsewhere for a safer return. Isn't that correct?" Jane pauses for a long breath, knowing that her next question might destroy any chance of an agreement, but she chooses to ask it anyway.

"So to answer to your original question, yes, we are elephants. But what is important to me here and now is, are you elephants, too?"

The room falls silent again as the Icelanders exchange eye contact with a look of discomfort and resolution. Krisuvik and Johannson exchange a few words in hushed sober tones, and there is again a pause. Johannson looks up at Jane with an atypically serious, and altogether, respectful gaze. Finally he speaks with an uncomfortable smile, as if Jane had just reminded him of some unpleasant responsibility requiring his attention.

"Jane, I believe we have all of the information we need to move forward." He rises and the rest follow in unison as he walks directly to her, standing closely and again taking her arm in his hands. "We are grateful for your visit with us today. This was a very interesting conversation. Please communicate the message to Mr. Brickman that he will have our decision by this Friday." Then, turning toward the door, he continues, "I apologize, but I must leave for another meeting. Hella, would you please see that Jane has the bank's car service? Is there any additional assistance we can provide during your stay?"

"Thank you, Magnus, but since the hotel isn't far from here, I'll just walk. These are my last hours in Brussels, and after

such a short stay, I'll spend them seeing a little of the city.
Thank you, though."

Elgar leads the way as they return along the cobalt blue carpet.
From the view to her right and slightly behind, Jane is suddenly
struck by the style and natural beauty of this woman. She wears
a translucent blue sea-island blouse, and the grey fabric of her
jacket is tailored to each curve, so that the open front, rather than
falling straight to her waist, is cut and darted beneath her breasts.
When she turns to Jane upon reaching the lobby, her body is
perfectly profiled in the sun-washed, frosted glass of the entryway.
Her straight blond hair is glowing in the light. She catches Jane
admiring her, and smiles. She removes her glasses, drawing her
hair back behind her ear, so that they are now eye-to-eye.

"Jane, the car is at your service while you are in the city, and for
your travel to the airport." Jane raises her hand to take Elgar's
linen business card. "Just call the number on the back and the
driver will come around to the hotel."

Jane turns the card over to read the Brussels phone number,
conveniently formatted with the city code. The handwriting is a
draftsman's font, as if jotted by an architect on a blueprint.

"It was a great pleasure meeting you, and I am hoping that we
will see each other again soon." As Elgar raises her arm to shake
hands, Jane purposefully reaches with her left to Elgar's waist and
embraces her with a *faire la bise*[1]. There's a split-second pause so
she can observe and enjoy the delight in Elgar's eyes, and then,
with a formal goodbye, she is gone.

---

1   A kiss on both checks of another, much as female movie stars often do.

Jane strolls the cobblestone walk across Le Grande Place toward
Bid Anspach and back to the Metropole. While marveling at the
architecture, she wonders about some now-nameless merchant
five centuries ago strolling this same square after meeting with
some long-forgotten Flemish bank (in these same guild halls)
about funding for the spice trade or gold exploration or even
a cod-fishing venture to the North Atlantic. She guards her
enthusiasm about the progress that was made this morning. Her
confidence that she has earned her salary today by doing the job
that Brickman sent her to accomplish, is tempered by the fact that
the results of the meeting are a matter of precisely what outcome
the Islandbanc is seeking. Had she, or had she not, identified the
key reasons why the Seven Seas business is important? Had she
created a clear path to the decision? Frankly, she doesn't even
care any longer. Her part is done. She has one evening left before
heading back to the States, and she will try her best to forget
business and enjoy the time. But as she approaches the hotel, she
can't shake one lasting impression from the meeting: the beauty
of Hella Elgar's profile. The sunlight at her back had seared itself
into Jane's brain photo gallery of truly sensuous images. She
reluctantly acknowledges to herself that the picture had affected
her physically, and it lingered. Neither certain as to why, nor
particularly eager to figure it out, she let it go. After all, in just a
day she would be 8,000 miles away.

Though immaculate, the ancient hotel has all of the
turn-of-the-century opulence and aristocracy found in a
full production of "My Fair Lady." It is not Jane's style, but
none-the-less, it is fitting for the Grand Dame of bygone Brussels.
As she enters the hotel she soaks in the dark oak and rich textures
of the place. She passes through the stained-glass lobby toward

the elevator, a Rococo, bronze, turn-of-the-century restored, open-cage lift, embellished with ornate metal work typical of the era. Upon entering the car, and while looking down at the control panel and selecting the number "8," she sees, in the corner of her eye, a flame of red stepping into the car beside her. Turning her face upward, she sees the unmistakable bolt of molten copper mane and flashing green eyes. "Melina!"

They instantly embrace and as the elevator closes. They just as quickly separate, as if they had caught themselves in an impropriety. Both step back, and, like school girls, check their dress and then each other, while awkwardly exchanging greetings and cordial smiles.

"Jane, have you received my e-mail?"

Jane is resolutely in "right brain" mode. The post-presentation endorphins have saturated her head, with the result that she has neither the presence of mind for, nor the interest in, another business conversation, even with Melina Bunge.

"Melina, I've been hoping to see you since I arrived at the conference. You look lovely."

As the ancient car slowly climbs, their opposed intentions collide in an "elevator silence." As if in mutual recognition of the foolish awkwardness, they share a laugh, and their smiling eyes come finally to rest on one another.

What is this?, Jane considers for a moment. As she scans the languid length of the woman leaning against the tooled railing that is bolted at hip height to the brass cage, she hears the slightest drumbeat of pulse building in the vale of her neck. It's oddly familiar and out of place, but then, at once, she recognizes the sensation. As a girl, she had hunted with her father, and he had taught her about quietude and patience as they stalked the morning fields of western Maryland. Occasionally, they would come upon an animal unexpectedly at close quarters, and her physical response was always the same. Some primordial predatory urge gripped her in those moments. Her senses would elevate to crystal clarity. Even in the pale light of the trees, her vision seemed to focus with binocular precision. Her heart would surge and, though she fought to control it, the beat would grow until it filled her head such volume that she was sure the animal would hear it and bolt. Space and time seemed fused as she would grip firmly on the rifle stock. Then, in one smooth motion to her shoulder, she would release the safety while gently laying the site into alignment with her right eye. She would aim at a point slightly above the heart. There was an almost hypnotic protraction of each second. Each detail of the kill, each motion spare and oddly detached, as if she were watching it all in super slow motion from some short distance.

And now the beat is stronger. The cadence is quickening like a mantra, pulling her into the presence and certainty of the events preparing to unfold. Jane turns with intention until her body is fully facing Bunge, now standing in stillness at the back of the car, trapped in the moment of Jane drinking in her Gaelic beauty. Bunge's expression evolves, like cumulus clouds before a storm, from smile, to resistance, then to resignation.

Jane has seen this face before. Once, while on an unintended tour of Lescot at the Louvre, Jane was stopped dead in her tracks before a small Madonna by an obscure renaissant named Bernardino Luini. She knew little about art, but was no less astonished by the preternatural expression that Luini had captured on Mary's face. The ancient oil image seemed to be radiant, and evolving even as Jane viewed it — first fine and tender feminine, then impassioned, then in the deepest thralls of capitulation.

Now, there is no periphery. Bunge's image fills the bronze filigreed frame carrying them aloft. She wants to speak, but when she tries she is unable. Words fail her. Jane's gaze is fixed hard-and-fast, penetrating. Bunge's eyes are in full dilation, black onyx pupils ringed in a corona of brilliant emerald. The trembling fusilli of red that frames her face is wilting. As her tongue runs between her lips, they exsanguinate, draining to feed the sudden thirsting core of her. The air feels heavy and pungent, as if they are climbing into a tropical canopy. The space between them infuses with the scent of Melina. It so pervades Jane's brain, that she suspends any remaining instinct to think. The rolling, rhythmic clickity-clack, the silence — but for softly slapping brass on brass — marks each submissive floor, ushering them on. Suddenly and somewhere in the ancient cage the Deagan chimes signaling surrender as it has in this age a thousand times — in war, in trade, in countless games of amatory charade. Finally with a jolt, *"Melina, mieux venir avec moi."*[2]

___

2 "Melina, come with me."

CHAPTER 25

The inverted, bright-yellow V-12 Cummins diesel engine slowly bleeds a thin rivulet of oil from its blow-by. It flows along the engine block before releasing into the seawater and floating in a thin thread up to an inverted pool around the flange where the power plant is bolted to the deck. An errant shaft from some chrome parts flares the beam of the diver's light, revealing a robin's-egg-blue hand, cuffed in red flannel, that has drifted into view. Three bodies hang against a small bubble of air at the corner where the bulkhead and the engineering deck come together. There is easy egress for them through a sealed hatch not 20 feet from where they came to rest. But, even with air to breathe, the sub-zero Bering Sea water can kill in seven minutes, and in the chaos of a 180-degree capsize, they probably had little chance to open the hatch.

But "brine freezing," as fisherman ghoulishly referred to death at sea by hypothermia, wasn't the only thing that threatened life in the belly of the capsized VEGA. A closer look shows that all three men suffered blows to the head. A ball of herring circles in and out of the light and nibbles at the torn flesh of a young toe-headed deckhand whose face drifted into the beam of light. A jagged, skull-exposing gash runs from the crown of his head in a crescent, over the temple, along the edge of his eye, and down to his cheek bone. The blow was forceful enough to crush the bone's mantle and expose the fibrous inner core. Perhaps as the boat flipped there had been no chance to secure a hold. Perhaps the bodies tumbled around in this greasy hole by whatever lethal force the sea dealt out that day. When humans battle crushing copper, steel, and iron block, there is no yield or compromise. In this tomb, a misplaced step or a bad heads-up will rip, burn, or puncture flesh and break bone, even when the skies are fair and the sea is calm. On August 8, off the Pribiloffs, the barometer was at 30.6 mm, and the Vitus Bering Sea was as flat as a blintz cake. There is no physical explanation for why 300 tons of sister ships should capsize so rapidly that no emergency could be sounded, and no hands could escape. The Coast Guard logs false emergency position-indicating radio beacons all the time, making it all the more ironic that with this worst of all calamities, there had been no beacon. No word. No chance. But here again, is it logical that all three able-bodied seamen bore killing blows to the head? And if a rogue wave or tectonic event had lifted them, why was there no buoy report, or radio calls from other boats operating in the area? The digital ballasting system would correct for a top-heavy weight of crab pots. And even if one system failed, and put one boat under, what can possibly explain this fate for the pair of them? What are the odds that both would go under?

Alaska exacts a toll from those who come seeking fortune in its bounty, its beauty, or in its sheer solitude. And though he had ordered men out before who hadn't returned, Akna Chernoff now knows from the Dutch Harbor Coast Guard diver's report that this time his judgment has played a darker role.

Chernoff is known for his genius in finding, fishing, and processing crab. He's better than anyone in the state. And he certainly understands the risks of loading the maximum legal number of fully geared, 800-pound pots atop the decks of twin 120-foot boats. But with the fishery limit of 250 crab pots, he had bargained hard with the Karensen brothers to overload. They protested, dug in their heels, and finally compromised at 225 pots.

It is Chernoff's natural way to press every deal he makes to the very limits of his advantage. True to his Russian chess-playing roots, he is skilled at reading the weakness in his opponent's position, and is fast at exploiting those weaknesses. Knowing that this was the brothers' first time in Alaska, and that they would be eager to make a name for themselves, he challenged them to show the other boats in the fleet that they had the "right stuff." He has a habit of opening all negotiations with impossibly high demands, setting his opponents on their heels before the conversation even starts. But at 250 pots, even the lowliest deckhand knows that the boats could never safely leave the dock. So Chernoff relented. But maybe not enough this time.

The brothers knew very little about the rogue waves that ply the north Pacific. Without a hint of the anger down below, tons of placid, blue-green sea water can suddenly raise a giant maul and blind side a boat with 80 feet of unmerciful physics. And if it does, and if a vessel's center of mass approached the water line, the boat could flip in an instant. A "no-count," down and out. But because risk only matters if you know about it, Chernoff chose not to disabuse the brothers with the truth. With the crab market at historic highs, he would do whatever was necessary to maximize the catch of every single crab that passed beneath his hulls.

So he made assumptions. He assumed the brothers would know the risks, and handle them. He assumed the newness of the boats' design, and the fresh onboard technologies, would guarantee their stability. He assumed the chances were low that, during the day-and-a-half outbound leg to the Pribiloffs, when the boats were at their most unstable and vulnerable setup, some simple, stupid twist of fate wouldn't screw it up.

· · · · · · ·

"Assumptions are always, always wrong," Brickman admonishes himself. Though he has complete confidence in Mika Vargas' translations during his meeting with Akiro Watanabe in Hawaii, the combined uncertainty of language, the 10,000 miles between them, and the tens of millions of dollars at stake, all dictate that he make no assumptions about their verbal agreement. He decides that the only way to assure there are no mistakes in the execution of their plan is to review each detail personally with Watanabe and his team, in person. He will cover every critical maneuver, and agree on contingency measures to cover any conditions that are beyond their control. His confidence is unshakable that Watanabe and Daichi Umi would hold up their end of the agreement. That is, he expects that Daichi Umi will perform flawlessly, according to the agreement as they understand it. But their agreement is entirely verbal — no details are committed to paper. There are no written references of any kind, except for a cryptic time line of acronyms they each had jotted down in their own coded hand as a mnemonics for the events ahead. But it is not enough. He will make no assumptions. There will be no surprises. He will go to Tokyo.

CHAPTER 26

As she gazes out at the iconic, multi-ring circus-tent design of the DIA terminal roof Jane feels for the ground effect that will cushion their touchdown on 34-L.

"Ryan, I'm here. We've just landed."

"Hey kid, glad you could make it."

The "Welcome to Denver" announcement overhead drowns out a portion of Jane's reply. ". . . sit down and discuss this meeting before we head out to Christian's? And by the way, are we meeting at his place?"

Brickman had arrived earlier, and had just checked in with Chernoff on the latest findings by the USGS and Navy divers on the capsized boats. Two crew members on the VEGA, including Todd Christian, had severe head trauma, which is suspected to be unrelated to the capsizing. There is some talk in Dutch that the Coast Guard was considering bringing in the FBI.

"Terri is still in bad shape, so I suggested that we take Carl Christian out to lunch, at 1:30 at place in Castle Rock called The

Old Stone Church. It's only about an hour south of here, and we can talk on the way. Meet me at Enterprise Car Rental, near baggage claim."

It bothers Jane that Brickman always presses about time. They have more than two hours before lunch. What's the big deal? This is a time when she needs to sit down face-to-face with him, and just decompress over the events of the past seven days. But there will be little chance of it happening. She knows the drill. Meet, drive out to customer, grab a quick lunch, back to airport, and gone. She has done it hundreds of times. Brickman will be relaxed, even entertaining, when he's with the client, but when it is over he will revert to serious and resolute, like a dog with a bone. One needs to approach him cautiously and be careful about what is said. When he's in this mood, he simply doesn't accommodate irrelevance or BS of any kind.

Jane spends the first 20 minutes recounting her presentation to the bank, including Krisuvik's promise to give them an answer on the loan agreement the day after tomorrow. By the time she has finished the story, the red Ford F-550 turns south onto I-25. Over the expanse of land to the east, groves of piñon pine and sage scrub hug every dry wash where the foothill ridges are deep enough to hold the water that flows down their flanks.

"Listen Jane, I don't like putting you in front of Carl so soon after the accident, especially since you've had so little rest. But it was our boat that killed his son, and you set it up for him to be there. You know him best. You gotta lead this."

"Ryan, I can't handle this by myself. You need to be there. If I get in trouble, I'm going to turn to you, and you need to take over until I'm together."

"Look, this is business. Business is about putting tough issues on the table and working them out. And this one, by the way, is going to take a couple of tries. Don't expect that we're going to walk in there and he's going to be open and accepting. This is a tough emotional situation. You're just going to have to deal with it and move on."

"Ryan, what are you talking about? Who cares about the damn business! His son is dead, and I put him up there!"

"Goddamnit Jane, snap out of it! We've lost guys before in Alaska. It's going to happen. Best thing for the dead is to deal with it, and press on. Leave it behind you. Do you understand? The business is what's important. I don't want us to lose one dollar in sales over the death of this man's son. You got me? You find a way to move forward from here with Christian. That's your job here!"

As she climbs down from the cab, the high, dry sun falls hard against her arms and face, as if she can feel the UV going to work. Spring sunlight is soft, but these clear autumn days bring a harsh light that exposes, browns, and breaks down anything left to the elements, particularly at the altitude in the foothills of the Rockies. Jane pushes up the bridge of her Ray-Bans, sets her shoulders back in an affirmative stance, and begins walking briskly forward, pacing herself slightly ahead and to the right of Brickman's commanding stride. They head across the parking lot and up to the entrance to the restaurant. She pauses at the step, while just

over her left shoulder Brickman's massive hand reaches up to open
the door for her. He motions her forward. As he does, she flashes
on the disfiguring scars and the ballast-rope-sized veins wrapping
his wrist and hands that she has studied like a road map of the
battling nature of the man. Often during negotiations, Brickman
holds his hands together steepled in front of him. Their broken
and wounded appearance often drive opponents to distraction.
More than one opponent has departed from his office flummoxed
simply because they'd been so damn intimidated by the mauls he
kept dangling before them as he spoke. Even shaking hands with
Brickman conjures a story of badly mended bone, mangled by a
crushing blow of the fist that left the first and second metacarpals
bowed outward. He always leaves the rest of the story to the
listener's imagination, but Jane has heard that it actually happened
while beating a man senseless who had made an ill-advised pass at
Brickman's wife.

As they enter the bar, Christian is immediately visible atop a stool,
facing the door on the opposite side of a square bar centered in
the front-room waiting area. He's pulling on a Crown Royal and
rocks, which he drinks like vitamin water. A bull-sized "Aldo
Ray" blond, he has risen up from a butcher job that he had
managed to find after his military tour. He has earned one of the
most coveted positions in all of retail: Chief of Procurement and
Merchandising for the nation's second largest grocery store chain.

Christian is known as cold-blooded and tough, but Jane has
somehow finally gotten under his skin. After visiting with him
a few times in his Denver office, he had agreed to join her and
Brickman for dinner while visiting San Francisco. After a half
dozen Crowns, he revealed that, while stationed in Vietnam, he

had belonged to a clandestine Army Special Forces unit known as the "Nightcrawlers." He told them an illuminating story about being trapped in a Viet Cong ambush early in his tour, ". . . like a nest of red ants," while on deep patrol beyond the DMZ. Under shredding crossfire, and with mounting casualties and their ammo spent, the five remaining platoon members decided, out of desperation, to call in air support. It was an option they had earlier rejected, for fear that the deep jungle cover was sure to result in collateral damage. But because, in Christian's words, "We were already dead," they agreed to call in the strike directly on top of their position. The strike ended up killing everyone except him and one other of the "'Crawlers." The unabridged version of their 60-hour ordeal of getting back to the American lines on foot had kept Jane and Brickman on the edge of their seats for the remainder of the meal that evening, which all three ended up drinking rather than eating. His love of Crown Royal is legendary, so heralded that, during the holidays, he accumulates a vast supply from Newday's vendors. He amasses sufficient amounts to hand out bottles like fruit cakes to anyone fortunate enough to score an appointment around the Christmas break.

As they approach him, Christian drains his glass and slides it forward for a refill, while rotating the stool into the barroom and placing his cowboy-booted left foot on the floor, then leaning forward so the mass of his shoulders propel him forward, and up and off the stool. As he rose, Brickman noticed something odd in his posture that looked both familiar and foreboding. Instead of raising his right shoulder as one would when reaching out to shake hands, Christian had dropped it, as a fighter does when he is preparing to throw a hook. Brickman is caught off guard as it sinks in that a punch is headed his way. Reflexively, Brickman angles his body to the right, just in time for the chin-glancing diesel piston of a punch that comes up from Christian's waist, just catching Brickman's cheekbone. It is a neck-wrenching blow that sends Brickman backwards toward the door, taking out two or three innocent barstoolers in his wake.

As the room begins clearing, Christian marches across the floor toward Brickman, his jaw set in the same pit-bull intensity that preceded the punch. Brickman is struggling to his feet, and preparing for the second blast, when Christian suddenly stops in a position just in front of, and swaying over, Brickman. His fists are jammed at his side, veins are popping out from his collar, then disappearing into his massive skull. His breath is a stinking mix of adrenaline and Crown.

"The Coast Guard tells us that Todd was murdered," he thunders, "and that he didn't drown with the others. If I find out you're in any way responsible for this, I'm coming after you."

Jane can see the combination of shock and humiliation on Brickman's face. Sensing that things are about to go very wrong, she charges at Brickman in an attempt to calm him down before he can lose his legendary temper. She shouts his name desperately to get his attention. But Brickman is enraged by the attack, and has been triggered to fight. Before she can reach him, and without a moment's hesitation in deference to the grieving father, he leaps to his feet and delivers a weak elbow to Christian's head. That creates a space between them that's big enough for a straight-armed jab to the eye with his right fist, dropping Christian instantly to his knees.

Brickman wipes at the blood that has begun spitting from under the flap of skin that had been cut between Christian's fist and his eye socket. He looks down at the man, who is now moored penitently to the floor by the blow just landed. Fist clenched, and breathing heavily over him, Brickman hisses between gritted teeth, "Carl, I grieve for you and your family, but I didn't kill your boy. Sympathies to you and your wife . . ." He breaks it off as a second wave of animal anger rises up within him, but this time he manages to control it.

With that, Christian raises his head, and Brickman reaches down to give him an arm up off the floor. The offer is rejected. Jane, who has been pressed up against the bar for the duration, now walks to Christian's side and stands next to him, struggling for what to say. She's stunned by the events of the past few seconds.

"Carl, I . . . You must . . . Carl, what can I say? I'm the one who arranged all of this. Forgive me. I'm so sorry."

With that, Brickman reaches into the inside breast pocket of his suit jacket and takes out a white envelope bearing the Seven Seas logo. "Terri and Carl Christian" is printed across its face.

"Carl, take this letter home to your wife. Open it in a week or so, when things get clearer for you two."

Brickman turns to exit the bar, placing one foot slowly in front of the other, moving cautiously through the dining room. Working his way toward the door, he reaches out to a passing table to grab a cloth napkin, dragging his hand carelessly across the table as he begins wiping away the blood, which is now spilling out of the cut where the bone ridge over his eyeball sliced through the top of the eyelid. Plates and silverware scatter across the floor, ringing out against the restaurant's dead quiet. Jane pauses next to Christian, then reaches down to help guide him back to his feet. His body is stinking of alcohol and ketone, and Jane tries, but is unable, to connect with his gaze, now fixed a thousand yards deep into the barroom floor.

"Carl, Brickman is an idiot. I am sorry. It's a terrible tragedy. I'm so sad for you and Terri. Forgive me. Ryan is a fool, and I hate him for this. He's a madman! Please accept my apologies."

Christian rotates his head weakly, up and to the left toward Jane. He is casting his eyes slightly, almost imperceptibly, in her direction, as if he has little intention of even seeing her, much less making eye contact. It is the look people have when they are passing someone irresistibly repulsive on the street — a look of disdain and pitiful understanding. And it is directed squarely at her.

What a son-of-a-bitch I work for!, Jane thinks to herself. She pulls a business card from her purse, and drops it in front of the bartender, who stands stunned in the lea of the cash register. She turns away and marches out the door and across the parking lot. She tries to contain her anger and embarrassment, but when she reaches the truck, she explodes.

"What the hell were you thinking, Ryan? Todd is dead. Carl and Terri are blaming us, and you go in and punch the guy out! Are you out of your mind?! Forget the $10 million in business, which is now never going to happen, by the way. Carl was soaking drunk.

He had no idea what he was doing! You'll be lucky if he doesn't sue you. And I'll be his first witness!"

They climb into the pickup. The tires spin out in the gravel and chirp onto the black top of the ramp onto I-25 north. The sun trails them, hanging up on their left in a crystalline blue sky. Blazing chrome flares are bouncing off the oncoming cars, and Jane and Brickman put on their sun glasses. Things begin to calm down as they pull off to visit a 7-11 a few miles up the road. Jane buys alcohol wipes, Band-Aids and beer, and standing in the parking lot by the truck, she cleans Brickman's face, and tapes him up. He changes his dress shirt for a Seven Seas blue polo from his overnight bag.

Brickman knows that the insurance check for $500,000 that he just delivered to Carl will not erase the pain of losing a child. But money, for better or for worse, is a powerful antidote for the myriad uncertainties that will haunt and hassle them at a time when grieving is the natural priority. Money can seem real and tangible at a time when much else is suddenly becomes so illusory.

☙

CHAPTER 27

Hoffman-UK's offices are above the recently completed Hampstead warehouse. The building still smells of epoxy paint, fresh-poured concrete, and the 10.5 million pounds sterling that it took to transform it from a vision to reality. With all of the hamstringing regulations and migraines in labor management — not to mention the sheer dedication of cash and resources to build a 15,000-square-meter store, then stock it, staff it, and make a go of it — it seems quite a commendable achievement. How did they manage to create the thousands of agreements necessary in such short order to get the project off the ground and running?

Charles Earlsfield has come to the realization that it was Hoffman-UK's certainty about the outcome they were looking to achieve that made it all work. Certainty is the path created by a people who transform visions into reality. And certainty grows exponentially into groups and organizations and whole societies. An agreement is the codification of certainty. The deal-maker is the person who sees themselves as that pathfinder — The Creator — of certainty in any given vertical of business.

Nigel Howard and Earlsfield are meeting at Hampstead to sign an agreement on king crab for Hoffman-UK's year-end holiday promotions. This is a big deal for Earlsfield, who estimates the value at £3.5 million in revenue during the fourth quarter. Furthermore, with a gross profit of 7.6 percent, it means a cash-flow contribution to the Seven Seas UK operation of a quarter-million pounds. That translates into a commission to Earlsfield of £22,000, at 8.5 percent. But he is having none of it. In fact, he assumes that the deal is DOA. He has rejected any pretense that the deal will be signed, and in the place of ebullience and self-congratulations he will remain, instead, skeptical and altogether obstinate until just the right moment.

Shepard's "Guess-Free Selling" training has taught him the power of "No" — the accelerating power of pressing each business agreement to the negative rather than the positive. The fundamental rule is that positive assertions are always perceived as false, even when they are made by trusted advisors. According to Shepard, it is partially an artifact of the way the human brain is wired, and partially due to the onslaught of programming the brain receives from advertising, from the moment of birth. The brain creates a natural defense mechanism to instinctively categorize any unfounded assertion as a lie. It's similar to the body's immune response. Therefore, it is dangerous to attempt to conclude a business agreement with a proclamation about how you or your organization will deliver some perfect version of the outcome that the prospect is seeking to achieve. Each prospect's mental "immune system" will automatically reject such a notion. And when it does, it becomes sensitized, not just to message, but to the messenger, as well.

Shepard says, "Even a life-saving organ will be rejected by the recipient if there is no immunosuppression. It's the same with deal-making. Knowing that unfounded, positive assertions trigger rejection by the prospect means that the only way to create certainty of agreement is with a heavy dose of reality."

This all makes perfect intuitive sense to Earlsfield, especially when dealing with the British, who pride themselves on being the masters of understated sensibility. That phrase "sticky wicket" is, after all, standard British parlance intended to diminish hysteria around any manner of human catastrophe, regardless of magnitude. Marketing and advertising campaigns with proven success in the U.S. and elsewhere predictably fail in the UK, due to the deep cultural aversion the British have to being sold any kind of product or service by anyone.

"If you want a prospect to sign," Shepard says, "shove them off the fence by asserting a negative. Talk about why the agreement might not work. Talk abut why it doesn't make sense. As you push away, they will instinctively pull toward you. This sets up a dynamic that whatever you propose or say next will be interpreted as truthful, correct, and acceptable."

Earlsfield slides his chair to Howard's four o'clock, which moves the cordial conversation to certainty.

"Nigel, I am excited about the prospect of doing business with Hoffman. This is our third meeting, and I gather your purpose is to conclude this business, or you wouldn't have agreed to it."

"Frankly, Charles, that isn't exactly correct. I still have a number of questions to cover."

"Well frankly, that's what I expected. In fact, I can see a few reasons myself why this deal might not make sense for Hoffman right now. I'm sure you have a few of your own."

"Actually, the issues I have aren't exactly 'deal killers.' But they are concerns we have with the merchandising and logistics that might turn out to affect the price."

"Nigel, I understand that they may not seem important now, but often it's the seemingly unimportant issues that have a funny way of blowing things up later. So, I'm interested in hearing what's on your mind."

Howard presents a short "laundry list" of logistical and merchandising issues sent to him on a spreadsheet by Tom Flowers, in Procurement, and Mary Smyth, in Merchandizing. Though most items can be easily managed with little or no cost to the factory, Earlsfield is guarded about his willingness to agree to any concessions that might alter the cost. Amendments to the regulatory labeling on the packaging have already been factored into the cost. But changes in the design of the carton have not, and, although this cost is minor, Earlsfield is intent on telegraphing to Howard that the price has been calculated based on a precise business formula, and is in no way arbitrary. Still, Howard presses for concessions, including a slotting allowance for the cost of placement on the shelves.

"Nigel, unfortunately there are no accruals or merchandising funds built into this model."

"Charles, your price is high. There are importers with more aggressive pricing — some at more than ten percent under the Seven Seas price."

"We do have crab we can deliver to Hoffman at a ten percent lower price, if that is what you require. We have three grades available, so we can accommodate you. But, it is my understanding that you are purchasing A-Grade product.'

"Your competitors have A-Grade also. We've seen samples."

Earlsfield senses that Howard has slipped into "buyers-school" mode, and that it's time to bring the conversation gently back to the outcome.

"Nigel, I dare say that your desire to land the best possible price is understandable. But presently, the demand is moving the market in the other direction. And the supply picture for Seven Seas is naturally more uncertain now, with the loss of the two boats."

"Yes, Charles, it was dreadful to hear of the accident. We, of course, sympathize with the company's position. But we need the best possible value we can get for our customers. All things considered, perhaps this just isn't the year to run a crab promo with Seven Seas."

Earlsfield sees the tactic for what it is: an effort to weaken him, and place him in the submissive position of having to chase the business. But he is not having it. Thanks to Shepard's training, he has made the conscious decision that he will never again cede control of the sales process. He has learned that deal-makers who have a structured plan for controlling the process have a 50 percent higher positive closing rate than those who don't. There are plenty of other opportunities, but in the end there is only one person he is accountable to — himself. And he refuses to dance like a marionette, just to see it all end in failure. He will maintain in control of the non-conditional elements of this sale. If this is a bad deal for Hoffman, this is the moment to kill it and walk away. But he knows this is a good deal. The merchandising opportunity has multiple advantages. First, it is an "exclusive" in the UK. So, for now, Hoffman will have little competition, particularly because of Seven Seas' high-quality standards. Further, Hoffman will capitalize on a hot item in a hot market, where the strength of the pound sterling is allowing them to buy any American goods at historic discounts. Plus, there will be Paul Stinbell's pestering to deal with, especially if Hoffman fails to realize the same success they are having in their U.S. stores. And then there is the time advantage. There is none left, and Howard will have to decide now, or risk seeing the whole deal collapse.

"Nigel, I'm sorry to hear you say that. This promotion is obviously important to Seven Seas, and to me personally. There is a strong history of success with our goods at Hoffman, and I believe that the competitiveness of the price and high-quality product we supply have been established. But we're running out of time. This is our third meeting to work out the details, and though we have made progress, unfortunately, we have failed to come to a final decision. Now you're asking us for additional concessions that seem to be moving us further from an agreement. I may be wrong, but the message I'm getting is that Hoffman-UK is not interested in doing business with us — that essentially it's over."

Outwardly, Howard appears unperturbed by the remark, but inside he is steaming. What the fuck is this, he thinks to himself. It's over? It's over when I says it's over! After all, I am the buyer aren't I? I have all of the privileges that go with the role, including that my demands will be conceded to because I have the authority to write a purchase order. I am free to respond to communications when, if, and as I wish. I can schedule meetings at my convenience, and with my agenda. I can report decisions based on my time line, not the vendor's. In negotiations, I can make any assertion I feel is necessary, true or false, to win my point. The one pleasure I have come to cherish most is watching sales people jump through hoops at my "beck and call." It is a form of entertainment that makes this job tolerable, and confers some special level of celebrity to me in my little world.

Now, Earlsfield has the gall to challenge all of that with two simple words? Howard is at a loss of how to respond. Does he simply concur, sparing his ego, and breaking off the conversation with no deal made? What about blow-back when Earlsfield reports the news back to the U.S.? Is he chancing a scolding from Portland if he blows up the deal? And what are his alternatives? Walking away from the promotion altogether? Patching supplies together from other vendors of dubious quality and unknown price? Good lord, he thinks, if the market gets hot enough, vendor commitments to deliver to Hoffman might disappear altogether. How will he cover the gap in the merchandising plan, the advertising plan, etc.? King crab drives dollars. How will he make up the lost revenues?

Howard rotates the chair back on its rear legs so far that for a moment Earlsfield fears he's going "arse over tit." As he pushes back, he raises his arms, clasping his hands behind his head. His expression transforms from one of pending perdition to a smile that explodes across his face. Earlsfield has the fearful thought that he has pressed things too far. Punctuating his words with an eerily mechanical laugh, reminiscent of a carnival fun house, Howard responds to Earlsfield's terminal remark.

"Good lord, old man, I wasn't going there, was I? Listen, we've talked it over. We know where we stand. We're going to do this deal for sure. Not to worry. It's just a matter of getting the details ironed out over the next few days with our folks."

Knowing that he now has Howard "on the mat," Earlsfield senses that it is time to drop his reticent posture and go for absolute certainty. He will not walk out without a decision, one way or the other.

"Forgive me, Nigel, but I think it's decision time." Earlsfield flips open his Bosca leather valise, tears off a sheet of the high-quality, lined white paper (it has a thickness and cotton content that one might use to handwrite a personal letter). "I'm sure you agree that we've worked diligently together on this promotion. So I'll tell you what, you take the pen . . ." With that, he slides the blank page across the desk, then, rotating the barrel of his black Mont Blanc ballpoint, holds it out to Howard. "Go ahead and draft whatever agreement you think Seven Seas can accept. I'll take it back to Jane for a decision by the close of business on Friday. Is that fair enough?"

Howard's smile is gaining in warmth, but he's still in tight-lipped resignation. It's checkmate, and he knows it. There's no way out. The implied "blank check" before him means that if he rejects the pen, then all his prior negotiations have been in bad faith, and, as Earlsfield has already stated, the deal will be over. And he will have to report it up the grapevine. In accepting the pen, however, he is tacitly agreeing to the deal as written. And if he makes any unreasonable demands now, they will be on paper, evidence that he is penny-pitching the deal to death. He has little choice but to write a deal that is fair to the proposal that has already been submitted by Seven Seas.

Howard takes the pen, and they both proceed to detail the key elements of the agreement. At the end, Earlsfield draws a line on the back, dates it, and holds it out for Howard's signature. He presents the pen with a certain flare, like an important armistice has been achieved.

"Nigel, assuming for the moment that I have an agreement from Seven Seas on the deal, when I call you back on Friday, when can I expect to receive purchase orders so that we can begin shipping from Alaska?"

With a little additional prompting, Howard explains the mechanics of the internal logistical process at Hoffman. Earlsfield uses his prior experience to bring up the activities that require coordination between the companies, and he is careful to map out the needed communications between appropriate people at the two companies, based on the information that Howard provides.

Howard walks Earlsfield back to the lobby. As they walk down the stairs, Howard proudly recites the specifications of the new building. Knowing that Hoffman has a culture of numbers, Earlsfield couches his questions in terms that are quantitative.

Their successful management formula focuses on measuring each and every element of their business model that might have an impact on the merchandising results of the stores. He recalls one interview with Herb Hoffman, in BusinessWeek magazine, in which he said, "We are relentlessly evolving our business toward what we can measure."

They reach the lobby, shake hands, and, as Earlsfield presses the bar of the door to exit, he suddenly stops and turns back toward the stairs, calling across the lobby. "Sorry Nigel, but I forgot to ask one thing if you don't mind."

Howard turns around with a somewhat concerned look, as Earlsfield takes a few steps back into the lobby toward him.

"What's the best time on Friday to call for you? Morning or afternoon?"

"Charles, anytime will be fine."

"I understand, but I want to be respectful of your time. Would you suggest the afternoon, say 1:45?"

They agree on a 2:15 call, and Earlsfield turns back to the door before stopping again, turning around, and retracing his path to the stairs.

"Nigel, I'm terribly sorry, but if I don't reach you at 2:15 is there a message I can leave that will ensure that you will call me back."

Howard raises his right hand to his forehead, "Well, you aren't going to make this easy, are you mate?"

"I just hate guessing about these things. I hope you understand."

"If I don't call back by close of business you have my permission to call Herb Hoffman himself and let him know about it. Fair enough? And by the way, send me a calendar invitation for the 2:15 call, OK mate?"

Crossing the parking lot to his car Earlsfield marvels at the acres of fresh asphalt. He marvels at the story that Howard had related to him about the entire opening of the building being delayed because the striping of the parking lot was postponed due to the worldwide shortage of titanium dioxide, a key ingredient in the needed paint. Uncertainties about demand, caused by the recession, had driven paint manufacturers to decommission production, which in turn caused available stocks to drop, which slammed the brakes on road and parking lot striping.

Uncertainty kills business, he mulls over in his head, and uncertainty kills deals. Guess-Free Selling has taught him to take the risk out of achieving the best customer outcomes by getting rid of the unknowns. He must strive to get detailed and granular on "What's next?" whenever possible, and stop letting his personal fear of the "client's truth" cloud the process of getting decisions done. Shepard's admonition, "You can't blow up a good deal," gave him the courage to press for the reality in every customer agreement. Through the training, he has learned that what he is actually getting paid as a sales professional is his expert awareness of, and ability to eliminate, the uncertainties that typically come back to haunt even the best "dead cert" agreement.

He punches the accelerator and kicks in the twin-plenum of his classic bottle-green Vandam Plas Rover 3500, sending him screaming up the ramp, and onto the M-25. Crossing directly to the speed lane, he is satisfied that he has achieved his intended outcome with Hoffman. Not that the deal was done. After all, there is no telling whether or not Jane will even agree to Howard's terms, though he is fairly confident she will. He is gratified that he has successfully created a "no-risk path" to the decision. And that he has successfully focused on the outcome that the customer wants to achieve. He maintained the control that was necessary to get them there, and when the moment was ripe, he had no reluctance about exercising his move toward a decision. He pressed for it until there was zero ambiguity about where they stood, and what was next. He had gone for the kill.

CHAPTER 28

Japan Airlines had just peeled the wrapper off a fresh 747-700 for Ryan Brickman's flight from San Francisco to Narita. He steps through the front hatch and turns left into the first-class cabin. He typically books a starboard seat on westbound flights, and a port seat when eastbound. But evening trans-Pacific flights are his favorite, free of the sun. All that matters is a window. He has had remarkable experiences sitting at a window. Visions and epiphanies that are bold, inspiring, and some of them altogether uncanny, so much so that he never attempts to share them, nor does he care one way or the other that he doesn't. He wonders how many other people carry around similar stories of 36,000-foot transfigurations of self-understanding. But again, it doesn't really matter. By his way of thinking the rest of the world has just enough of a line on him to make him uncomfortable, he doesn't want them any closer. He doesn't give a crap about the opinions of others. His guiding principal is that everything around him is transient. Only he is permanent and unfailing. To Ryan Brickman, his life will never, can never end.

After taking his book from his leather satchel and tossing it into the magazine pocket, he settles into seat 1-A, a SkySleeper Solo seat. The plane reeks of the latest in engineering and strikingly handsome design. As a businessman, Brickman has always marveled at Boeing, and seen the company as the epitome of what humans can achieve in the complex task of engineering and design innovation. Land at any international airport anywhere in the world and you'll see row upon row of 747s and 777s. At Haneda, Japan's national hub for most domestic flights, Brickman has seen no aircraft other than the stubby short-haul 747s.

To his mind, management has only two priorities: 1.) Keep one foot firmly planted in the problems and issues of today, and 2.) Keep the other foot firmly planted in the dreams and aspirations for the future. He presses his teams at Seven Seas to solve their problems among themselves, and not to come to him to authorize the fix for any problem under $10,000. His one requirement for any decision for systematic change is to always challenge the change in terms of its measurability. No matter how great an innovation sounds, if they can't measure the impact, it won't adopted. Seven Seas breeds into the organization the importance of hard wiring the future into every essential system and process.

In spite of his combative history with his Asian counterparts in business, Brickman has a MacArthurian attraction to the Japanese cultural aesthetic. The goof-ball nobility of the Japanese people fundamentally appeals to him like no other society he has experienced. Japan is a tribe of 100 million members, clinging to the tectonic edge of a hard spit of land, and teetering atop the seven-mile-high cliff that creates the eye socket of the massive skull-form map of Asia. To him, the city of Fujiyoshida captures the essence of Japan: a thriving society living in the constant and real shadow of the lethal magnificence of Mt. Fuji. From a

Darwinian perspective, this environmental dynamic, together
with the homogeneity of the populous, goes a long way toward
explaining why the Japanese are the Japanese.

He is reading the new book recommended by Jane called
"Guess-Free Selling," by David Shepard. As the plane continues
to climb into the night, he pulls Shepard's book out of the leather
pocket on the side of the seat. He stands up to retrieve his reading
glasses from his leather satchel in the overhead bin, and makes eye
contact with a distinguished-looking, bespectacled Japanese fellow
with salt-and- pepper hair and an inviting smile.

He holds out his hand, inviting a shake, "Ryan Brickman."

"Toshi Ohgami. Pleased to meet you."

Brickman has come to learn that the Japanese generally age more
gracefully than Caucasians, and often their looks belie their true
age, often by decades. This gentleman is no exception. Though his
grey hair suggests late 40s or early 50s, his face has the naïve and
youthful appearance of someone half that age.

"Stop Guessing," he says. "I have read it. What do you think
of it?"

In ice-breaking mode, they continue briefly about the book, but
that quickly evolves into a conversation about each other's work.
Ohgami is a former Institute for Advanced Studies Fellow, now
studies trends in global private enterprise at the Hoover Institution.
Brickman is always easily drawn to conversations with bright
people, especially when business is added to the mix. When that's

the case, he digs like a miner for any insights into the reasoning behind the person's views and opinions.

"Ryan, understand that in Japan everyone the same. Look over a crowd at rush hour in Ginza. It is a sea of same thing. Everyone on same page. There are very few uncertainties. Do you understand? We all know same language. We know same religion. We know about each other's families, and how they behave with one another. Everybody the same. We are land of uniformity. Our key axiom is '*Deru kui wa utararu*', the standing nail gets hammered. You understand? We don't create. We imitate and we refine."

When Brickman mildly protests that Japan, and now China, are beating America in the competitive marketplace, the Japanese gentleman dismisses him with an academic's authority.

"It's geo-politics. No country will exceed the U.S. to create wealth and opportunity. It's the immigrants, over hundreds of years. Built by immigrants. We do not have this advantage in Japan, where everyone is same, thinks same. Immigrants think and act differently. Living in the U.S., even if you want to get comfortable, you cannot do it. And it's the culture. There's no escaping it. Everywhere else on the planet you can go on vacation, relax, let your guard down. You just can't get away with it here in the U.S. The immigrant ethic of work and sacrifice is relentless. There is always someone nipping at your heels who will work harder, who will do with less, and is more ambitious. They're in your face every morning when you go to work.

"Look," says Brickman, "the U.S. exports $600 billion to China, but U.S. buys $1.8 trillion from them. I'm not buying that immigration is solving our problems."

"Ryan, this is temporary with China. I know for certain. America is paying to bring China into the 21st century, like they did with Japan and Germany after World War II. It is a cycle that will soon decline for China, but turn upward for the U.S. because the U.S. is becoming incredibly lean and productive, ready for the next surge in innovation. The U.S. is the opportunity factory for itself and the rest of the world. The emerging countries produce things, even some services. But the national struggle to succeed, to embrace and make change is in the DNA in America. It's a permanent part of the engineering of the country. The U.S. isn't aircraft and agriculture. It's one gigantic non-stop, bust-ass, force, asking 'What's next?' It's the last-chance laboratory for creating the impossible out of thin air. All because of a prevailing immigrant desire to 'be somebody.'"

Brickman is piqued by the implications of what he is hearing. In essence, because of the country's massive and isolated geography, and its history as a destination for some of the smartest and most ambitious of the world's people, this eternally magnetic frontier can never be superseded economically by any other country.

"And here's truly magic part," Ohgami continues. "Any country that has learned, or has been conditioned by necessity, to be relentlessly dissatisfied with the status quo, and who, through sheer will of mind or constant challenge to their economic survival (and has developed a compelling appetite for "What's next?"), will become economically indomitable. Period. And America has been the specialist in engineering just such a business environment for more than 200 years. There is literally nothing that can stop it."

Brickman's brain is full from this conversation, and he turns to the window to rest for a moment. The plane is on the great circle route, currently heading west-northwest, just south of the Aleutians and will slowly turn to west-southwest, heading into Tokyo. At altitude in the dimmed cabin he can make out the constellations on the southwestern horizon. As a fisherman, he learned to read the positions of the stars reflexively, and from his seat tonight, he can easily see Antares, the red star in the center of Scorpio, and cream-colored Venus, the brightest object in the sky rising above Antares and to the west of it.

"Mr. Brickman?"

He is suddenly relieved of the burden of more thinking by the supremely beautiful flight attendant, dressed in a traditional ornate silk *cheongsam*.[1] Her face is an only slightly more Asian version of Audrey Hepburn, a la "Roman Holiday," and she bears the intoxicatingly demure expression that Japanese females have perfected to ensnare the attention of even the most obdurate male. The classic, sleeveless, form-fitting silk dress is cobalt blue with a gold-embroidered choker collar. The fabric is so fine that as she faces him, he can discern each subtle surface feature of her breasts, abdomen, and loins. When she turns to serve Ohgami, the dimples at the top of her hips disappear, appearing again as she bends at the waist. A deep cleft forms as the fabric falls between her buttocks, disappearing again as she rises to a ramrod-straight posture. As she turns back to face Brickman, his eyes seize hers,

1 A body-hugging, one-piece Chinese dress.

and, in an instant, Brickman's characteristic unflappable cool is shattered by a moment of pure virile instinct, as a predatory smile sweeps across his face. His look becomes so intensely libidinous that it prompts a flush of blood through her entire body, even penetrating the veil of alabaster makeup covering her neck and face.

Brickman has ordered the Japanese meal from the in-flight menu, and the first course is miso soup served in a red-and-black lacquered bowl, with a fine bone-china spoon bearing JAL's logo. He decides to sip the soup from the bowl, and as he lifts it to his mouth the plane suddenly lurches in an errant pocket of air, causing him to spill the entire pungent broth and tofu into his lap.

"Ah, shit!" He leaps from the seat, mopping the soup from the sodden pants of his Seven Seas blue-on-blue jogging suit. The attendant instantly glides up to his side with a terry-cloth towel, carrying with her the realization that he will be spending the next ten hours and 15 minutes sitting in supreme, first-class luxury with a crotch full of fermenting soup.

After the meals are finished, dinner drinks are served, and the lights in the cabin are dimmed. The atmosphere drifts into a quiet reverie. Most passengers doze or are headphone deep into the entertainment systems built into their sleeper seats. All is quiet when the attendant suddenly appears at Brickman's shoulder carrying a folded bundle of cotton cloth, enclosed in a plastic wrapper. She leans over, and with her lips only a few inches from his ear she whispers, "Mr. Brickman, please come with me."

He unfolds himself from the seat, and follows her back to the crew area, which forms the bulkhead of the first-class section. Two of her fellow flight stewards busy themselves in jump seats in a dark corner as the attendant places the bundle on top of the beverage cart and turns back to face him.

"Mr. Brickman, please remove your pants."

She gently bows at the waist, but this time with an affirming nod forward and left, like a cat seeking attention. It is as much an order as a request.

"I will clean and dry them and return them to you before we arrive in Tokyo. You can wear these pajamas."

And with that, she reaches out and unties the draw string on his jogging pants while instructing him to remove his shoes. As she leans down to pull the waist band over his hips, he senses a pleasurable dynamic, similar to when he is having his inseam measured by his tailor, a Korean woman whom he has relied upon for years to adjust his waistline or fit a new pair of slacks. He has found it characteristic of Asian women to be more comfortable around men in almost any situation than their Western counterparts. The sensation of a woman's hands on his clothes is always exhilarating. And though she performs the task of removing his pants with epicene indifference, he finds the experience of having her tugging at is pant leg both intimate and irresistibly evocative. He lets his imagination run with it.

Standing before him, her silk garment outlines each exquisite curve of her body. With his eyes, he traces each feature: the nape of her neck, her lips. He pauses at her eyes, perfect in their elliptical eyeglass frames, the ancient bronze setting drawing him in deeper. It is like the thrill of walking in the dark in a strange place. He imagines the heated scent of her clothes, the silk woman with the geranium and orange hair — thick, black, and mysterious. First a veil, then a rope, then a cave to explore, exploit, and exhaust him.

Truncating Alexander the Great, he has confided to his doctor in shameless arrogance that, "If it weren't for sex, I'd swear I was immortal." His battles with fear of physical danger on the high seas have taught him a presence with, and dispassionate acceptance of, the cards that are dealt. "If my number's up, my number's up." To him, angst over the future is a pastime for teenage girls, not grown men. Struggling with the vast uncertainties of building his business, he has concluded that gut decisions and fearless action are the only activities that deserve his attention. Everything else is secondary. He gives spirituality no quarter in his life, choosing instead to ignore the unknowable altogether, and otherwise adhere to Disraeli's admonition: "All sensible men believe in the same God, and no sensible man discusses it."

Sex alone is irresolvable with logical methods. The proximity of an attractive woman is morphine to him, and he is heartily and joyfully addicted. It is that single irresolvable vulnerability to which he hasn't the least interest in putting up a defense.

After a jet-lagged, five-hour nap, a shower, and some tea, Brickman is picked up at his airport hotel at 5:45AM by a black Lexus sedan.

The driver gently rolls out of the hotel portico for a quiet start to the three-hour drive to the Hakone-Ginyu *onsen*[2], a modern *ryokan*[3] on Lake Ashi, near the foot of Mt. Fuji. Having dozed off for the first hour or so, he awakes as the car ascends through the thin clouds that cloak the artisanal rice paddies and terraces, now washed in the pre-dawn pallet of soft greys and blues, reminiscent of the ancient sumi watercolors. Looking out into the morning reverie, he spots ghostly silhouettes drifting among the garden rows that are deeply contoured to the rising foothills of this magnificent and fundamentally vulnerable land. He considers the logistics of the upcoming meeting, and wonders about Mika Vargas' commentary in her e-mail: "Mr. Watanabe enjoys to hike. Please, Mr. Brickman, that you bring climbing shoes."

The region he is visiting is otherwise known as the Japanese Alps, a chain of volcanoes and tectonic peaks that bisect the island. At the eastern end is Mt. Fuji, rising 4,000 meters over the five lakes that encircle it. The lakes create picture-postcard reflecting pools from any point on the compass, evidenced by every manner of calendar, postcard, and T-shirt on sale in the 7-11's "gift shop," where the driver has stopped for a break.

Returning to the car, Brickman switches on the reading light, and picks up one of the three financial daily newspapers that have been placed in the car for his convenience. After only a few minutes his impatience over comes him. Dropping the paper, he reaches for his well-weathered, black-leather satchel. He removes the red note book, which records substantially any issue, problem, dirty stick, or broken machine requiring his deliberate decision, along with

2   A Japanese term for hot springs.
3   A type of traditional Japanese inn.

any important actions with done dates. He rifles the pages until he finds his instructions to himself regarding the Daichi Umi meeting, and begins reviewing them.

He always insists that any Seven Seas business plan be developed in granular detail, on paper, prior to being executed by the company. His self-imposed insistence on writing down his plans is a testament to his "walking the walk." But, over the years, he has also learned that he is faster and more certain of getting business done by spending time "noodling out" a plan in his head, rather than on paper. He has learned to develop entire business models in his mind, including the financial details, saving him immense time and effort, and allowing him to focus on qualifying opportunities based solely on the fundamentals.

For this meeting, he has done both. The purpose is to assure Watanabe that the coordination of the specifics of their plan to short the king crab market is flawless, with no confusion about actions or timing. The outcome of the talk is to assure total coherence on the final plan, and to gain confidence that he can count on Watanabe to follow through, as agreed, when the chips are down. The process Brickman has planned for today is, first, to present the elements of the plan as he has imagined it unfolding in time. That will reveal any obvious vulnerabilities on the Tokyo side. Then he plans to challenge Watanabe on the execution of each of the tactical pieces by turning the tables and asking him to justify his assertions. If he is being deceived about their agreement, and Watanabe is contriving to use knowledge of the short plan against Brickman, the impact on Seven Seas could be disastrous. Requiring Watanabe to defend his commitment to each of the plan's steps, face-to-face, is a proven method for exposing the truth. When the inflection point in market price arrives, it will become critical for the two of them to be of one mind. Only then are they assured the control that is needed for a comprehensive collapse in the market, while extracting maximum gain from it.

Crashing a market occurs in three natural periods, reflecting the topography of hope that "long traders" cling to, as their positions disappear before their very eyes. Rather than dumping the price overnight, Brickman plans to precipitate the drop in three stages. Each level will be punctuated by a brief round of buying before resuming with synchronized, tactical actions, and reasserting the downward trend. After the first round, he will order an upward revision in the cold-storage-holding number, thus destroying confidence. By the third drop, any trader holding a king crab position will be hopelessly upside down. Their bankers will have become aware of the unraveling market, and will require their customers to restate their inventory values. The reduction in the borrowing base will trigger redemptions of the credit lines, and that will, in turn, mandate further liquidation of stocks, and even greater selling pressure in the market.

Brickman has written guaranteed downside protection into all of Seven Seas' sales agreements. Those clauses insure that no purchase orders to the company can be revoked on the basis of market conditions. To the contrary, most of the sellers in the market seek to lock-in the high prices, and have issued fix-priced orders to their retail and food service customers. In a topping market, these agreements are vulnerable, because major buyers will almost certainly renege at the first signs of an inventory sell-off. If so, this will have the effect of ballooning the total open inventory positions among the players. If that happens, the market will certainly enter the "oversold" stage, where forced sales will allow Seven Seas and Daichi Umi to buy crab at steep discounts off its natural equilibrium price. Brickman's worst-case is five percent net. The more likely case is eight percent, and the best-case is a nearly $12 million profit from the short, based on the current orders he has in hand, and his short inventory position. He guesses that Daichi Umi holds nearly three times the marketing position of Seven Seas, putting their potential gain at more than ¥2.5 billion. To Brickman's way of thinking, this is an outcome Watanabe can not afford to disregard.

The switchback road climbs from the lake valley. It's lined with cedar trees, which lean over the road, forming a passage way to the front of the ginyu onsen. The car gently wheels left into the Belgian-rock drive before circling the courtyard and coming back under the *porte cochère*, which flanks the massive hardwood doors leading into the lobby.

He has spent 16 of the past 22 hours sitting. Finally liberated from the car, he stretches to free his 6-foot-2 frame of knots and kinks, smiling with anticipation of the workout, shiatsu, and hot mineral bath that await him after getting settled in his room. He inhales deeply the intense aroma of the rich tephra-grown cedar, thick in the air, rising up from the lake 100 meters below. As he's finishing his stretching, his eyes rest on the view through the open doors and across the entryway into the ryokan. The landscape seen from the balcony beyond is so high, yet so close, to the lake that it gives the impression that the entire floor is somehow suspended out over the electric blue water. The whole scene is framed magnificently in the giant hewn-cedar beams that arch above the lobby.

The driver follows him into the lobby, carrying his bag. Brickman pauses in the center of the room to take in the extraordinary surroundings, while the driver proceeds directly to the front desk, drops the bag, and begins conferring with the manager on duty. After a few minutes, a woman dressed in a burgundy kimono appears from a door cut into the rosewood paneling behind the reception desk. After speaking briefly with the driver in a series of hushed and smiling exchanges, the driver departs and the woman turns and walks toward Brickman. Even from a distance, the radiance in her face is stunning. Her skin is pale, and completely natural, and her waist-long hair is pulled back into a thick, chestnut braid.

"Mr. Brickman, I am Ran. I welcome you to Ginyu onsen. I hope you enjoy your stay with us. Mr. Watanabe and Miss Mika Vargas are here, and will be joining you in the onsen in two hours. Please follow me to your room."

On the way, they exchange pleasantries, and Ran informs him about the ryokan's amenities. Her plain linen kimono of fine-flowing weave trails her as she walks to the elevator that drops to the rooms facing the lake below. Brickman is intrigued by her unadorned beauty, and, in his typical unabashed style, takes full stock of her body as they stand together waiting for the ride down. His eyes come to rest on hers, and he employs them with little restraint to pantomime his pleasure in her native good looks. Like another's deep appreciation of art, he takes in the finest details of her face before the bell tone of the arriving car breaks the moment, and they step inside. As they begin moving down, the electricity escalates, and his close proximity to her in the small car becomes wonderfully intense.

"Ran, maybe you can help me. I have been traveling for days and need some exercise and a massage. I really need a good workout. What do you suggest?"

She remains remarkably calm and at ease by his riveted attention. With his question, the elevator begins descending, and likewise, so does her composure. She turns slowly toward him as a warm and inviting smile blossoms across her face.

❦

CHAPTER 29

The Coast Guard's preliminary report revealed nothing about the cause for the loss of the VEGA and SIRIUS. In the highly superstitious fishing industry, "widows" — fishing boats that have a history of deaths on board — don't last long, and are typically unsellable. Having lost their entire crews on their first trips, these two boats will be sold for salvage, and the company that managed to refloat, rotate, and tow the boats into Homer are eager to strip them, sell the parts and scrap, and recoup their investment. The National Marine Surveyors team has just visited the boats in Homer, signed off on scraping the hulls, and has faxed a copy of the release to the Seven Seas office.

Akna Chernoff is standing on the dock at Homer Boat Works, looking out over the Homer inlet through the gap between the VEGA and SIRIUS. He's holding the Coast Guard's Preliminary Report, and the NMS release on the boats, and mulls over the finding that there is no apparent cause for the capsizing. The suggestion is that a rogue wave is to blame. Chernoff had requested a U.S. Geological Survey seismic report for the day that the boats were lost, and it had come back with, "We found no evidence of a seismic event in the Gulf of Alaska/Bering Sea region sufficient to raise a wave of the magnitude needed to threaten navigation in the region."

He paces the dock, scanning the two vessels for the slightest clue that might point to the cause of the disaster. He turns up his collar against damp wind coming up off the sound. The chill is wrapping around the boats and the nearby steel fabrication shed, and collecting atoms of bone-cold iron and depositing them down his collar to the middle of his back. Frustrated, he begins walking back up the dock toward the gate when a horn blasts over the water, queuing the end of the day shift for the shipfitters and boilermen working the boats. He turns to look back down the dock as the men, one by one, climb down from the scaffolding that surrounds the rigging, and head for the gangway to the dock below. The crew is meticulously stripping the two boats of everything salvageable, and as they file past him, he looks into every eye for a spark of comprehension. The last man off the boat is a grizzled welder, likely in his 50s, but with the engraved face and silver hair of a man 20 years senior. His Dickies are tarnished with soot, and they're duck-taped in a spots where a raw cut of angle iron had snagged him, or a white-hot steel cinder had make it past his rawhide apron. As the man passes Chernoff he pauses, removing his welders gloves, and looks back over his shoulder at the Vega.

"You the owner?"

Chernoff reaches out his hand to grasp the man's right claw. "I was. Chernoff, Akna Chernoff. And you?"

"Ben Cannon." He pauses again to look back to the boats. "Coast Guard figured out what caused the wreck yet?"

"No, nothing yet. Why do you ask? Got any ideas?"

"Sure, but if you say I told you I'll deny it. And, in fact, you might want to deny it yourself."

"I'll be the judge of that. Go ahead, shoot."

"It's the load line, the Plimsoll mark. I'd say it's two to three feet too high. Safe enough, so long as it's tied up at the dock, or in easy water. But if they loaded to that mark, the boat wouldn't even make it out to Dutch, much less the Pribiloffs, especially if it started to blow."

Chernoff turns on his right heel and looks up at the circle-bar-shaped mark that denotes the legal load limit for any commercial vessel operating in territorial waters. The Plimsoll is also known as the insurance line, because loading beyond the Plimsoll automatically violates a ship's seaworthiness certification, and voids the insurance policy. But why, he wonders. A mistake? Impossible. It's basic arithmetic, using the tonnage and the displacement of the boat. Plus the National Marine Inspection Service inspects the mark. If this guy is right, it's got to be either deliberate or negligent. But who would willfully cause the death of 13 men?

Chernoff's mind is whirring, "The Coast Guard wouldn't miss that. They would have picked it up in the preliminary inspection, long before you guys went to work on it."

"It ain't none of my business. I don't know for sure, anyway. Coast Guard certifies the marks. Probably they've already figured it out. They're being careful in what they say. If it's their screw-up, you'll never hear about it. It could be the surveyor, too. Or somebody here at the boat yard. The Lloyds guy has been here two days. Didn't run a tonnage calculation, so maybe he'll miss it, too."

Chernoff's gut grips in a knot. What's this guy's angle? Blackmail? If he's right, the GD lawyers will love it. Seventeen million tied up in the boats and crew, plus the aggravation that goes with it. He stares into the man's proud, defiant eyes. Extortion? A warning? No, that's not it. But I'm not taking any chances. He reaches into his pocket for a stack of cash, and tucks his business card between a trio of Franklins.

"Here Ben. How about this stays between you and me?" Cannon looks down at the money, cocks his mouth in a half-smile, and releases a short snort through his hair-filled nostrils.

"Listen Mr. Chernoff, keep your money. First this is Union Alaska work. I make that much in an hour overtime. Whoever did this is likely here on the docks, working for Anacortes Boat Works."

With visible effort, Cannon cranks his neck up and to the right to face Chernoff. It's as if years of welding have fused the muscles and bones in his neck. Then he raises one woolly eyebrow.

"Hell, we might even know who it is. But we'll deal with it our own way. We don't need the feds or the newspapers crawling around down here. Nobody's going to hear about this from anyone on this dock. Now that the boats are decertified, we'll have 'em cut down to the keels before there's a chance to ask any more questions. It'll all be over, if we can help it."

Chernoff has an uncanny gut instinct about judging people, and his gut tells him that this fella's word is good. He will keep an agreement.

As Cannon pulls a pack of Camels from the breast pocket of his union suit, Chernoff crams the cash (and his card) into that pocket. "Skip the overtime tomorrow, Ben." Then he turns and walks away. "And give me a call if you hear anything else."

Chernoff carries the sick feeling that if there are any suspicions about blame for the wreck, it could trigger an investigation that could last for years, especially with a government agency involved.

"Ryan, they don't have a clue. I talked with the Coast Guard office in Anchorage. The book is closed. Suspected rogue wave. Too many pots on the deck. That's it. Thirteen men gone, and as far as they're concerned, it was simply bad luck. Wrong place, at the wrong time, with the wrong load plan. The boys on the dock in Homer know the load line is what's wrong, but they're not talking, in case it turns out that it's one of their own union guys who's responsible. They don't want the spotlight on them."

Chernoff went on to tell Brickman that the insurance payment is in jeopardy, so he has called Mike Molinari to ask about the consequences.

"Ryan, your loan is callable right now. The bank is being flexible, but they don't have to be. If they get wind of an issue with insurance coverage, their collateral evaporates, and they'll call in the loan. That's it. That's the way it always goes."

Brickman doesn't at all like what he hears, "But what the fuck is insurance for? It's to cover us in case of catastrophe, damnit!"

"Oh, you'll get the money, eventually. But if there's a hint of trouble, they'll take every justifiable path to delay the payment process so they can state your claim as a future liability, instead of a current one. It's all about the stock price, Ryan. Short term is all that matters."

CHAPTER 30

Win Tongbang's office hangs like a huge stadium suite over the massive cold-storage facility, which covers the right triangle formed by 5th and Central in the Los Angeles warehouse district. The interior is 1980s Ridley Scott: dry, aged, futurist science fiction, a la Chinatown. Tongbang's desk is nested in a Rube Goldberg of cabling and computer screens — beacons flashing out pricing information across the dimly lit room from the raised platform at its center. His affection for '50s furniture creates a style that fuses Mandarin and mid-century Madison Avenue.

Two steps below are the cubicles of Tongbang Brothers' market minions — the country managers who feed him a stream of offers from around the globe, plus updates on the state of fisheries' production from every coastal time zone on the planet. Tongbang has trained his global suppliers to stay up late and rise early to make offers and negotiate with him directly by telephone. The benefits of consolidating his buying into a set time-period has an added tactical advantage: sleep-deprived people seldom negotiate the best bargains. But more often than not, there is no bargaining at all. There is Tongbang Brothers' price and terms, or there is no deal. A couple of failed negotiations, and the producer is dropped from the vendor list, a fate that most seek to avoid at all costs. Tongbang's decisions are absolute, and when they're paired with his ruthless attention to profitability, they provide him a remarkably simple and dispassionate formula for running his business.

He punches the flashing button on his cell phone and begins to speak. Suddenly, the voice at the other end cuts in nervously.

"Win, the boats will be decertified tomorrow. I'm pushing the crew to begin stripping them down as fast and as soon as possible." Lauren Hapides' voice attenuates to a whisper. "Win, there's talk on the dock about the boats being overloaded. They're talking about the line. This is not how we planned it, Win. It was supposed to be an accident, not this disaster."

"You worry too much, Lauren. You did what I told you, right? So the boats are condemned. No more investigation. It is over. This week is the Moon Festival, and I have made a donation in the name of Chang'e, goddess of rebirth. With this loss, the bidding for king crab will escalate, and drive the market even higher."

"Yes, I went into the design software and changed the effective length back to 124 from 142 on the load-line calculation. It's now back to the original number. And I erased the trace on the document. If they audit the numbers, it will look clean."

"See? No problem! You are the salesperson. Always sell anything for the right money, correct? You made the deal, you sold it. It's over. Take some time, and forget about it. You have the money now, Go away and enjoy it. Go to Disneyland!" Tongbang cackles at the irony in his own suggestion. "Yes, come down to LA. I take you to go see Mickey Mouse."

Hapides had been a managing inspector for Fraternite General de Surveillance in Alaska. FGS provides production, quality, and grading certifications for U.S. and EU customers for fish packing plants. Because she is an expert in the king crab and salmon fisheries, Tongbang Brothers "recruited" her to expedite their certifications and inspections in Alaska. The arrangement was eventually discovered, and she was terminated. But, in time, Tongbang arranged a sales position for her at Anacortes Boat Works, as part of a deal with Tongbang Brothers for ABW to take over management of their flagging vessel construction business in Qingdao. Tongbang adds, "What about Brickman. What is he planning?"

"He's shopping for new boats. I've taken him some offers, but so far, he hasn't moved. I don't think it's going to happen at the numbers he wants to pay. He sounds eager to get it done, like he's got orders to fill, but it's going to cost him more than the insurance check to replace the tonnage, that's for sure."

"I understand. Good, good. Now add some fuel to the fire. I am interested in buying a king crab boat with quota. That will raise the stakes for Mr. Brickman. Let me know what you hear."

He punches the phone off, and slides it across his desk, then picks up an old, battered pink intercom. The receiver is encrusted from years of service. He barks pidgin Mandarin into the phone, ordering his crab buyer to give him an updated position statement

on king crab, and to find another 60 containers — two million
pounds — of B-Grade king crab at $3.25 per pound or better.

He takes a scrap of paper out of his pocket, and flashes
his assistant on the intercom. He snaps a phone number
in a clear crisp monotone *"Si-yi-wu; ba-er-ba-er-qi-er-qi.
Jaio Jane Dreyfuss."*

CHAPTER 31

Jane rolls over in bed as the late morning sun cuts through a split in the curtains, sending a spike of brilliance that blazes off the orchid-white, 1,000-thread linen bedding. She's been deep into jet-lagged sleep. She always sleeps naked for the simple pleasure of feeling the fine cotton against her skin, like another kind of lover.

Two messages show on her voice mail. Brickman's said that he is returning from Tokyo after ". . . a very successful meeting with Watanabe. Listen Killer, you did it! I got a call from Og Johannson and they've given conditional approval of the credit line for Seven Seas. Terrific job. Hella Elgar and Og are meeting us in San Francisco tomorrow to go over the papers. I have Mike Molinari coming down from Seattle to check the details. Listen Jane, I need you there. No travel required. We're meeting at the office at 10, then we'll go to the Tadich Grill for lunch. You sold this deal. Magnus Krisuvik and his team loved you. Og tells me that Hella Elgar wants to hire you. I told him, 'Not a chance. She doesn't speak Icelandic.'"

This is good news for Seven Seas. Jane feels good about Brickman's comment from Johannson, which both gratified her, and reassured her that Brickman valued the work she'd done.

"I know you're lagged, but I need you at the office by 9:30 tomorrow. With the loan done, I've got Lesterman and Chernoff coming down here. It's time to move on the plan."

Jane spins in the sheets, and, for a moment, is feeling elated at the news. She has sold them on the loan, "elephant" and all. The weight that she has carried since Brussels about whether or not her boldness had paid off is lifting. And then, of course, there is seeing Hella Elgar again. But, in spite of the happy message, Brickman had said nothing about talking with Mike Molinari about her stock as he promised her he would. And the thought of it brings her hurtling back to earth. Again, there's the dread that this deal is never going to happen. The aggravating notion returns that Brickman's promise of equity is a pipe dream — just another clever manipulation device that will never see the light of day. He is a bastard, but she's the one who's falling for it. Why blame him when he's just doing his job. There is no chance of equity partnership. There never was. The sudden despair is eerily reminiscent of the scene in the Water St. Deli after pitching her business on Wall Street. And while that memory hurts, it's time to move on. Better to sell apples on the street corner and own her life's work. She would eat out of a trash can before she would ever again subvert her self-reliance. Brickman has created his own outcome, and it is up to her to keep fighting for her own. She can no sooner achieve his dream than live his life. It is time to stop trying.

She momentarily forgets that there's a second message on her phone. As she punches the "1" button she wonders who would be calling her this early from San Diego who wasn't already in her contact list. She is brought back by the recording of a very formal woman's voice, clearly Mandarin, but with a clipped British accent. It speaks of old world Hong Kong.

"Miss Dreyfus, this is Miss Singbi calling for Mr. Tongbang. He would like to speak with you on an urgent matter. Please call his direct number at your earliest convenience."

Tongbang? What the hell is this? She has never even spoken with him, much less met him. But years of dealing with the constant rivalry of Tongbang Brothers has invoked an irritating Win Tongbang "avatar," characterized by everything he seems to personify: genius, ruthlessness, and a diabolically oriental enigma. Its presence has hounded her at every new business opportunity she has pursued. Now he is calling her about a meeting? What could this be? No guessing. She immediately picks up the phone and begins dialing.

"Win Tongbang, this is Jane Dreyfus. I have a message from Miss Singbi on my voice mail. What can I do for you?"

"Hello, Jane Dreyfus. May I call you Jane?"

"Absolutely." Jane hates permissions being used on her. She uses them often on prospects with surgical precision, but she dislikes it coming from Tongbang because he somehow manages to make it sound so damn sincere. "Listen Win, I don't know why you called, but let me be straight with you, right up front. You're a competitor, so I don't like you. You're Tongbang Brothers, so my opinion verges on disdain. Lastly, all I need is for some fisherman to find out that we're talking, and we'll both end up in front of a grand jury investigating price fixing."

"Jane, you are straight with me. I am straight with you. Carl Christian told me about what happened in Castle Rock, with Brickman. This is not my concern, but I was saddened to hear about it. I want to help you. You are very talented. I would like you to work with me. It will be a partnership, and you will earn more than you do at Seven Seas. You will be the boss. Run your own show."

"Win, I appreciate your call, but I'm already paid very well, and I have the freedom to do what I want to do, when I want to do it."

"I understand that maybe you don't like us. We have made mistakes, and I have some regrets about the reputation of my brother and me. But we have a new direction now. We have an agreement. Before, only I understand that we are limited in the clients we can do business with because of our reputation. Now, my brother also sees this truth. So, what I am offering you is your own business, where I will support you silently. Understand? You will have ownership. It will be yours to run as you wish, to build a new name."

Jane is stunned by Win's offer, and, for a moment, she's at a loss for a response. What his angle here? Nothing is straight with this guy! She decides to dig a little deeper by going negative.

"Win, I appreciate the offer, but like I said, I'm happy where I am, and I have no reason to want to change. I'm sorry, but I don't see any purpose in . . ." Tongbang interrupts.

"Jane, I'm sending the plane to pick you up this afternoon at 2:30. Come down to San Diego and we'll talk for an hour. If you do not like what you hear, I'll have you back in San Francisco for dinner. You have my word."

"Win, I'm really not interested."

"The plane will be waiting for you at the CX Aviation Hanger at the north end of Airport Boulevard. And my car will meet you at the airport."

Jane checks the clock, then buries her face in the pillow. 8:45 AM. She still has time to get to the office and think over the call before making a decision. What could be the cause of Win's sudden interest in hiring her? Could it be Brickman's fight with Carl Christian in Denver? Did Christian report back to Tongbang about the brawl, and her shock at Brickman's callous reaction? Was it about their argument afterwards — about embarrassing her, and humiliating a desperate man who had just lost his son? It sounded like the chance she has waited for all her life — a chance to start her own business, to run her own show, and hire the sort of people she wanted to work with. No more insulting the Japanese, and punching out the dock workers. No more mercenary's tactics, risking whatever it took just to win. Always, it's always just about the winning.

Cranking the steering wheel of her silver Porsche 911 into a parking spot in front of the hanger, she exits the car just as a shiny Cessna Citation screams overhead. She pauses to watch the wheels tuck neatly into the wings. There are few things in life more fascinating than flight. As a girl, her hero had been Amelia Earhart. She loved everything about the aviatrix: her daring, her passion, her business acumen. She'd studied Earhart's exploits in branding herself. She loved the story about the launch Earhart's chain of exclusive boutiques, located in department stores in major markets across the country. Earhart had convinced one of her aviation sponsors to finance her in a venture to produce a line of active women's wear, styled to capture the spirit of flight. Her bold, somewhat masculine, designs made an important impact on women's fashion of the day, but her insistence on fine silk and linen fabrics conflicted with her commitment to make the clothes affordable, even to working class women, and the venture soon failed. But Earhart's steely determination resonated with Jane on an heroic scale. She has treasured Earhart's spirit of ambition since she was a girl, but so far she has failed to bring it to fruition. The question that badgers Jane most is, "Why not?" Maybe this is her shot. Maybe Win Tongbang is giving her the chance she has been waiting for — a chance to build the Jane Dreyfus Company.

Grabbing the leather haversack that she keeps as a permanent accessory on the back seat of the car, she walks to the FBO's entrance as a 737 roars past the checkered barrier not 1,000 feet away, then banks right in her direction. Jane enters the hangar's lobby, walks toward the door leading to out to the planes, and drops her bag near the refreshment counter. There's the familiar prickling sensation as the smell of the Jet A-1 fuel and precision engineering fills her nose. As she steps through the door into the hangar, the view sets her heart racing. A Cessna, a GulfStream, and a Dassault Falcon sparkle under the golden sodium-vapor lights, and she is mesmerized by the sheer beauty of their .8 Mach lines caught in a freeze frame. A gangly, grinning string-bean of a man, dressed in blue-yellow racing-striped overalls, and with a Gumby smile, approaches her as she steps beyond the orange "Authorized Personal Only" stencil on the floor. He flips open a drop-top clipboard, and, after a quick check, raises his eyes from the passenger list to confirm her credentials and her onboard refreshment order.

She is pressed into the seat as the Falcon rotates steeply upward. The pilot gently nudges the throttle, inducing that characteristic airborne calm that returns each time the earth and all its contents begin peeling away. She rifles through a mental catalog of memories that accompany her each time she ascends out of various spots around the planet. Adventure, escape, anticipation, ambition, but never reluctance, and never regret. Going and doing seemed to be the universal solvent when reluctance and reticence gummed up her ability to think critically and take action. She has learned to count on travel to lift her spirits and motivate her, regardless of the struggles and issues she is leaving (if only temporarily) behind. She thinks a little differently when breathing in the stratosphere. Who knows, maybe it's the ozone, she'd often wondered.

CHAPTER 32

"Carl, listen," Win Tongbang says, "I have four million pounds of king crab for the holiday ads in last quarter. You match Hoffman's $19.99 to start until they get loaded up, and then run a bogo[1] every other week. We'll destroy Hoffman. Understand? They will never see it coming."

"What's my cost?"

"Don't worry, Carl. You'll make 55 percent, and 20 percent net on the bogo. You'll own the market. But more than that you'll make the others look like fools."

"That's great Win, but I'm hearing talk that the market is too strong. The yen has been weakening, and if it continues to weaken, the Japanese might go off the market. And if they do, the price is going to drop like a rock."

Carl Christian understands that in Japan, large commodity seafood markets such as crab, shrimp and tuna have such great liquidity and well-defined demand that they are often traded

---

1   a retail slang term for "buy one, get one free," a common form of sales promotion

like another form of currency, especially during volatile foreign exchange. In like fashion to oil, food products trade globally in U.S. dollars. But with Japan, the dominant fish buyer, the value of any international speculative play in seafood can be judged primarily based on its ultimate value in yen. A weakening yen can trigger a fall in the dollar price that Japan will pay, and in a top-heavy market, the pricing can suddenly capsize, trapping anyone carrying large inventories at the time.

"Carl, don't worry. I will cover you on the market downside. You let me know what you are hearing, and we will change the price. You understand? We are looking out for each other, right? Just remember, for me to pay you, I need to make a profit."

Mun Tongbang approaches his brother's desk with a scrap of paper marked with one number, "167%."

"Win, this is very unlucky for us. We 67 percent over position limit for king crab. Nearly $44.5 million total. Bank will be calling on this and I must have answer prepared. They will no longer accept excuses. We must have delivery commitments. They want to see purchase orders."

"I will have Newday send purchase orders to cover the October deliveries. Meanwhile, invoice a third of our stock to Certified Wholesale to get it off the books until we need it for November shipments. We'll move it back on and invoice it before we need to report the borrowing base to the bank."

"Win, the bank auditors aren't stupid. If they catch us manipulating the inventories, they'll pull our credit line."

"I'll call the state controller's office. They'll get the bank off our backs. If that doesn't work we'll go to Hong Kong."

"Win, do you realize what can happen if we can't liquidate these stocks at the price you've projected? It could ruin us. You understand that?"

"Mun, we have worked through many difficult times in the past, haven't we? And we always find way to out smart the *gweilo*.[2]

We will do it again. Don't worry."

---

2 A common, derogatory, Cantonese slang term for non-Asian foreigners.

CHAPTER 33

Akna Chernoff walks along the dock, pauses, and looks out over the breakwater at the grey pall of the top of Alcatraz, floating above the morning mist that hugs the surface of the bay. A cold morning, seemingly worse than Alaska. An isolating cold.

"If I can just get through this season," he says out loud, to no one, "I'll have my nut, and to hell with the rest of it." His cell phone begins ringing in his breast pocket.

"Chenoff."

"Mr. Chernoff, Ben Cannon, in Homer."

He scans his memory for the name, but his thoughts are miles away. Suddenly, the name snaps into place. "Cannon, yeah sure. What's up, Ben? What do you have for me?"

"You told me to call if there was any news up here."

"Shoot."

"Coast Guard is hush-hush, but there's talk that the Feds were tracking the Russians. A sub."

"There are always Russian subs in the Bering. Why the fuss?"

"No, this time a big one. Typhoon-class, picked up on satellite off the Pribiloffs, near where the boats capsized. They say the sub deballasted, and the turbulence turned the boats."

"Waves can't sink one crabber, much less two. Unless they hit 'em."

"No strike. The hulls are clean. But the boats were running side-by- side, and both were overloaded. The load lines were wrong, and the boats couldn't handle the surge from underneath. It flipped 'em. They have radio transmissions from the sub. Listen, the feds are all over up here, and they're interviewing everybody, shutting everyone up. That's all I have."

As Chernoff walks west along the pier, headed for Brickman's office, he barks into the phone, "I appreciate the call, Ben. Keep it to yourself. I'll be back in Homer on Thursday. Call me then."

፮

CHAPTER 34

"Carl, I don't apologize. But now's not time to talk about it. Maybe in a couple of months or so. There's little we could have done for you, I know that. But . . ."

"It's over, Ryan. It was over at Castle Rock. I wanted to tell you that. We're going to have to live with this. Both of us. We sent Todd up there. We want someone to blame. But, that's it."

As Brickman hangs up, he stares out over the cold chop that stretches from the breakwater across the Golden Gate to the Marin headlands. He recalls the stories that the Klondike crew told about the risks on the Barbary Coast — the currents and the winds and the sharks. There were men who never expected to return, and got their wish. And there were those with guts, who always seemed to find a way home. Whenever something goes wrong at sea, the Italian fishermen have a saying, *"Coraggio ti tiene."*[1]

Daichi Umi will begin limited selling by their wholesale business into the Tsukiji Market at mid-day, California time, this Monday, while bidding the market lower through their trading arm. The market news will make it across the Pacific the next morning.

---

1 Courage keeps you.

Akiro Watanabe will issue orders to Daichi Umi's Seattle office
to withdraw from the fishery and begin selling off available
U.S. stocks.

Brickman calls Akna Chernoff. "Timing is critical. We need this
to be choreographed perfectly so that Watanabe is convinced that
he can trust us. He must be certain that we will do exactly what
we say we are going to do. Akna, I need the receiving barges to go
down to 50 percent capa"Music enters our bodies, commandeering
the pulse in our veins, and reminds us that pleasure isn't a matter
of feeling good but of feeling more alive." over the first 48 hours,
beginning at 12:01 a.m. on Monday. Find any excuse you can,
but I want to be off-line when the boats start calling in for price.
I want the electricity to go out on Dutch receiving, except for the
generators running the freezers. Keep it up until midnight Tuesday.
I want your plan on my desk before tomorrow morning, outlining
how you will get that done."

"Ryan, first the boats are going to hit the roof if you pull off
the market. They'll quit us altogether, and then we'll have no
production at all."

"When they're hungry, they'll come and eat. When we pull off
the market, what are the other packers going to do? Keep buying?
If they want to let this market take them down, it's their own
business. I'm worried about myself. Let the boats do their own
arithmetic. Akna, everybody's going to call you and ask what's
going on. We need to keep this looking straight. We don't want the
Attorney General's office after us."

"Ryan, they can't touch you for colluding with the Watanabe. He's in Japan!"

"If the boat owners get hot enough, they're going to find a scapegoat, and I don't want it being us, that's all. Take the calls and tell 'em we're doing a company-wide inventory audit. What's our position looking like right now?"

"If we include the Newday business, our position is negative by nearly $21 million, through the end of the year, not including first-quarter business. About one-third deliverable over each of the next three months. If we need to cover October at today's prices, we're a push."

"We'll more than double that position before this is over. Jane will have all the national chains on speed dial. When the market starts sliding, we'll begin slowly hammering these guys down. When we hit $5 for medium legs and claws, have your brokers start buying, but no more than $1 million per day. If it drops below $4, we'll double up. Got it?"

"OK. But where do we stop?"

"We stop when the market turns, and not before. If it goes flat, we'll back off until we see where it's going. When it turns down, keep bidding lower."

"What if it turns up? Do we keep buying?"

"When it turns up we are going to sell a little to get a feel for what's next. We'll keep testing on any strength until our offers are snapped up. When that happens, both Daichi and Seven Seas will start bidding it up until there are no offers left."

"Ryan, Tongbang Brothers is booked very long on Number 2 Grade crab. Right now, there's about a buck difference on the price, but if the market tanks, that spread will explode. You won't be able to give away the Number 2s, and the stuff will be all over the market."

"Don't buy one pound of anything but A-Grade. Do you understand? And I want inspections on every lot. No excuses. If there's no paper, take a paid option on the goods until we can get an inspector in there to look it over. If the market tanks, the retailers will only take the good stuff, and I don't want to be anywhere near any black shell."

CHAPTER 35

As Jane exits the Net Jet Terminal at Gillespie Field she scans the town cars and limos lined up at curb side. She's looking for the "TB-38" plates. From Jane's years on the wharf. she knows that 3-8 is the luckiest number combination in Chinese numerology. If the success of the Tongbang Brothers is any indication, the numbers are working. Win Tongbang enjoys an almost mythological reputation in the industry. His C-level influence among many in the retail food and distribution business is legendary, and a listing of Tongbang Brothers' important political contributions runs from local supervisors to the governor's office and beyond. Their strategy is simple: no facet of their business interests is left to chance. Uncertainty is unacceptable. Tongbang has developed an uncanny instinct for predicting the outcomes in changing commercial conditions, and for capitalizing on them by bringing the important variables under his control, whenever possible. And control to Win Tongbang means cash. The secret to his success is that he never gambles. When he places a bet on a piece of business, it is a sure thing, and he is an artist at using cash to determine outcomes.

The car turns onto San Fernando and immediately climbs to the Golden State South. Instantly, a Don Henley song begins drifting in and out Jane's head. There's something about Southern California that appeals to her, but not in a permanent "no-place-like-home" way. It's the attraction of perpetual transience, the freeway on-ramp sensation: Keep moving or it'll run you down. It's the "right here, right nowness" of the place that means there is no past, and no history in a land of constant reincarnation. There's only connecting the next dot. Maybe this will be the big one — the big payoff this time around. And here she is, headed to meet her arch enemy to talk about joining him. Isn't her reasoning the same. How do the dots connect in the story of her last seven days? The boats, Carl Christian, David Shepard, Melina Bunge, Charles Earlsfield, Hella Elgar, and now Win Tongbang. Where is this leading? Could it be, finally, her big payday?

The car smoothly rolls down East Harbor Drive toward the warehouse district and skid row. The weather is an overcast cocktail of high clouds, fog, and smog that gives the air a close, isolating feel — like being alone in a crowd. As she steps from the car, she is taken back by the surreal and odd assembly before her. A massive pre-war warehouse, painted on one face in oriental green, part jade and part Christmas ornament. The street side still bears the faded remnants of a billboard-sized classic California agricultural ad: "California Orange Growers — Golden Fruit from the Golden State." Below the motto is a dazzling señorita, all smiles and cleavage, effortlessly cradling a 50-pound basket of fruit that's nestled against her loins. Jane wonders how this one got past the United Farm Workers Union.

There's no activity on this side of the building, just a plain steel door marked with the address and "MB Import/Export

Company." As Jane approaches the door, the solenoid buzz of an electronic lock triggers her reflexive grab for the handle. Above the door is a video camera scanning the parking area. The entryway splits three ways: to an emergency exit about 100 feet to the right, straight ahead to a vanishing point down a dimly lit corridor, and 30 feet to her left, an elevator. It's an equally dark passage, but spot-lit by a shaft of bluish light originating somewhere above in the ceiling structure. As she approaches the elevator, another of the red bug-eye cameras peers out from the left of the door, just above the call button. In the dim silence, she reaches out to push it, but before her finger connects, there's a slap of copper on copper. The humming of hampered amperage echoes down the short shaft as the winch motor engages and sets the greased cables slapping as they lower the car from the floor above. She has an overwhelming sense of dread as the car trips past the positioning switches and lurches to halt. The doors rattle open. The elevator's interior appears as old as the building itself, and though it seems that, at one time, this was the private entrance of some banana baron and his lieutenants who ruled over citrus during cinema's golden era, it has since fallen into disrepair. She is at once taken aback that two brothers who control a dominant market share of U.S. imported seafood operate their business from such a remarkably grungy and devolved location.

When the door opens Jane is astounded at the Fabergé egg of the room, decorated from floor to ceiling in the baroque Chinese style of red and gold. Focal point of the waiting area is a massive, carved gold-leaf frame of serpentine dragons that encloses a Goliath robe of red silk, so finely embroidered that only upon closer scrutiny can she see that the adornments are fine thread, and not paint. The twin doors at the end of the room are interlocking bronze dragon heads, each the size of a small dog. As she approaches them, they open, and Win Tongbang reaches out his hand to greet her.

"Jane Dreyfus, it is an honor to meet you. Truly an honor."

Tongbang has a comfortable smile, and his eyes are genteel and inviting. His close-cropped grey hair, and very thick horn-rimmed glasses, give his face a Mr. Magoo-like appearance that is disarming. Jane watches him as he carefully makes his way toward her, not without some care. It is clear by the way he scans back and forth as he walks that his poor eyesight handicaps his movements. A wave of instinctual simpatico overtakes her as the impression of his genteel manner blends with her empathy for his apparent physical challenge.

"Win, it is a pleasure to meet you. Thank you for the invitation to visit, and for your generous accommodations in getting me here."

"I never fly, myself. But I so enjoy talking with people who do. Did you enjoy your flight? Was it exciting."

"The plane is beautiful, and it was a magnificent flight."

"It is the looking down. I can't stand looking down. I have a compulsion to want to jump. Quite crazy, right? But I cannot control it. It isn't fear. It's the vertigo that overpowers me."

"That's unfortunate. I do very much enjoy flying, the freedom of it."

"Yes, but tell me Jane, I did not ask you to join me to talk about flying, right?"

"Yes, about a partnership."

"Yes, exactly. Jane, I want to make you rich. There aren't many people in the seafood industry with your capabilities. Do you understand? If you have intelligence, you can make money. I believe you have it. You can succeed with your own company. I believe that, based on what I have heard about you."

"From Carl Christian?"

"Yes, from Carl Christian. But also from others in the industry. People I respect." Pointing the way, Win continues, "Come to my office, and we can sit and talk."

They walk through the trading floor and enter another elevator, which opens directly into a reception area with an admin-type seated at a large teak desk just to the right of an oversized, but plain, pressed-bamboo door, hand calligraphed. Win's office is on the floor marked 5 on the elevator button, but it is actually on the fourth floor of the building. As he passes the assistant's desk, she begins speaking Mandarin. Her tone is acutely deferential, but there is an urgency in her voice, almost desperation. Only two words are distinguishable by Jane's ear: "Lauren Hapides," and the moment they are spoken, Win flashes a concerned look at Jane, barely moving his head, but stretching his eyes to the edge of their sockets to detect any reaction from her. Jane recognizes the name, but makes no immediate connection. Her response is indifference. The exchange passes without further attention.

The office is tasteful, but furnished sparingly. The décor is austere to the extreme. In contrast, the wall behind Tongbang's desk is adorned with scores of awards and photographs, including every important California politician, and various celebrities. The giant picture window provides a panorama of downtown Los Angeles, while an interior window on the eastern side overlooks the shipping bays, and provide a clear view of the cargo movement in and out of the warehouse. Jane is intrigued by the grid of seven video monitors that are mounted behind his desk, each displaying a different location along the loading zone on the dock. Tongbang sees her watching the activity on the floor below.

"Jane, I can tell you the market by watching the movement of boxes on that loading dock. It is easy, if you just pay attention every day. It makes me a lot of money. I can teach you as well. And it can make you rich."

Jane reaches back to the instruction she had from David Shepard about "no guessing." She isn't going to waste time with this conversation if it isn't directly relevant to her primary goals of earning more money, and owning her own business.

"Win, help me to see what you have in mind for this partnership. What is it that makes you think this will be a worthwhile conversation?"

"Tell me what you want, Jane. What can I offer you that will get you to leave Brickman and move down here with us?"

She understands that Tongbang is reflecting the question back to her, and she wonders whether he is just being evasive. But before she can answer, he jumps in again.

"Jane, I will be honest with you. I'm not young, and I'm not very healthy. I do not have talent like yours working for me anywhere in this building. This is a family business, and I have partners to answer to who do not do the work. It has been all for me to carry the business forward, and I am growing tired. None of my people are up to your standard. Plus, you have had a powerful teacher, with great experience. This is valuable to me."

"Ryan Brickman. Yes, he is a . . . a genius." Her words sound sincere, but the hesitancy in her voice, and her shifting in the chair, signals some conflict between what she is saying and what she is thinking.

"Carl told me about what happened in Denver. How gracious you were, in spite of Brickman's behavior."

"He lost control, that's all. It was a mistake, and he knows it."

"Jane, my people tell me that Mr. Brickman can be a violent man. That he can be unpredictable."

"Listen Win, I'd rather not discuss Ryan if you don't mind. Can we talk about why I am here? Tell me about the outcome you are looking for from this conversation."

"I would like to start a new company, the two of us, separate from Tongbang Brothers. I will be a silent partner, but I will work with you to build it up. I will provide the money, and you will control the business. It is that simple."

"But why now, and why with me?"

"As I've said, you are talented. Your reputation in the industry is excellent. You are well trusted. As you know, Tongbang Brothers has had some past problems with our reputation in the industry, and it has hampered us in our ability to grow in certain areas."

"You seem to be doing quite well, from all I hear."

"Jane, no great business ever started clean. When you dig into it, in any big company you will find one person who did whatever was needed to make the business succeed. Carnegie, Rockefeller, Vanderbilt. They were all bad guys in their day. But they adapted as they grew. You don't think Carnegie killed anyone to save his business? These men left behind them some of the greatest corporations in the world. But they didn't start out that way. We have had a bad reputation, perhaps. But the past is past. Now it is time for me to look to the future, and this means that I must change also, if my business is to keep growing. And this means that I must look past Tongbang Brothers."

Jane's head is abuzz. Killed anyone? Is that what he said? Surely he was just trying to make a point. Regardless, he was right. The reputation of Tongbang Brothers is tarnished, no doubt about it. Some buyers are afraid to get near them, regardless of the pressure.

"I am proud of the business we have built, but I'm not proud of how we got here. But, also, I do not regret it. I need to move forward, Jane, so I am offering you this chance to help me in a way that will make you rich. Do you have the ambition to run this business? To run your own show? Your name over the building? Do you have the desire to make real money? I am not talking about $175,000. I am talking about $300,000 to $400,000 a year or more, plus your equity in the business."

Jane immediately wonders how he possibly knew her salary. But it doesn't matter. His questions are so on target that she is biting her lip to control her breathing, which is now getting over the emotional impact of finally being offered a chance that she has dreamed about all of her life. He has her hooked, and she knows it. This is her shot, and there is no way in the world she is going to miss it.

"Win, can we talk about the money. Tell me about the equity. What is the split you have in mind?"

"75 / 25, with the opportunity to accumulate additional shares based on business results. But let's discuss this when we meet with my brother. He is the wizard of these things."

"But I thought you mentioned that it was you who will investing."

"Don't worry. Tongbang Brothers will fund it, but I will be the majority partner, of course. But tell me, what about your salary? Is $250,000 a sufficient base to start off with, say, with a percent of the gross profit after break-even?"

Again, there's a flicker of uncertainty, and a slight change in his story. How can Tongbang Brothers fund the business, while

Tongbang keeps the controlling interest? Oriental bookkeeping? Let them figure it out. Anyway, it seems insignificant, compared to the $250,000. Bonuses are typically seven to eight percent of the net. If she crushes her numbers, she can easily add 50 percent more to her earnings. That's life-changing money. While she can barely contain her excitement, she decides to test his commitment anyway.

"What is your time line, Win? When do you have in mind for getting this all done? By what date would you like things up and running?"

"You tell me. When are you ready to go?"

"I would say about ten days. I will be ready to leave, say, the first of the month."

"Perfect. Ten days it is. I will make the arrangements."

It all seemed too easy. But the prospect of a $1,000-a-day salary is making her feel much more comfortable about the decision.

"Jane, just one thing that is very important to me — it's essential if we are to be partners. My business is built on loyalty. You understand? We must be able to depend on each other. I am going to make you rich, but I must know that you are loyal to me."

Jane senses that the other shoe is about to drop, and her antennae go up.

"Win, I am loyal to myself, not to the company I work for. Let's be clear right up front."

"Jane, I am happy to hear you say that! Naturally you come first. It should be that way always. Same with me. Even my brother understands that my business interests must be protected first, then Tongbang Brothers' interests. I do not try to fool him on that. And I am glad that you feel the same. But I am talking about your loyalty after you. I am not talking about the company. I am talking about me, personally. I expect loyalty from my partners."

"If what you are asking is whether I would cheat you or our company, the answer is absolutely no. It's not my way. Once we become partners, my work is to benefit our company. I'll do what's needed to serve that responsibility to the partnership."

"I already knew that about you, or we would not be having this conversation. But I wanted to hear it directly from you. Jane, so far, I have asked nothing of you. I have presented you with this opportunity and explained how I believe this can, this will, make you rich — a multi-millionaire."

Millionaire? Jane Dreyfus, daughter of a merchant mariner, working her way through night school? She deserves this, doesn't she? It seems to finally make all the sense in the world. She is smart. She has killed herself to get where she is. All those years of paying her dues, and now it is all falling into place. But there would be a condition.

Tongbang continues, "I'm going to ask you to do something for me that will prove to me that you can be a loyal partner. And I will even explain why I'm asking you for it. But you must promise me never to reveal it. And if I find out you have failed me, the partnership is off. Do you understand?"

There's an easy answer and correct answer to his request. "Well, I'll tell you, Win, that it depends on what you are going to ask me, because I'm still kind of worried about that 'killing someone' comment you made a few minutes ago."

His head rolls back as a cackle of laughter from deep within his solar plexus rises to the ceiling and returns across the unencumbered chamber walls and floor. The laugh is amplified and distorted in a confusion of echoes that is finally indistinguishable as a laugh or a kind of wailing howl.

"No, no. Of course not. Nothing like that. What I am going to ask is this: Are you prepared to break off from Seven Seas and join me, or do your allegiances remain with Ryan Brickman."

"Go ahead and ask."

"I need the Seven Seas position report on king crab, and I want you to get it for me. It is a condition of our agreement."

Jane is caught off guard. Her mind starts rapidly processing: OK, position reports are important. They allow you to figure out what the net stock availability is on a commodity, (Sales + Orders) – (Inventory + Purchase commitments). If the positions are long (+), then there is exposure, if the market goes down. If the number is short (-), there is exposure if the market goes up. Tongbang has a long position, and he wants to see if he is in jeopardy. Except for the obvious ethical compromise, would she provide this information for a chance at a million dollars? Of course! After all, hasn't Brickman repeatedly promised her stock, and an ownership agreement? Hadn't he?

"One condition." Janes speaks cautiously. "I will deliver you the report in exchange for a signed employment agreement, with the following conditions: 1.) I join at one-third ownership, 2.) Options to 50 percent within 60 months, based on the numbers, and 3.) Salary is $250,000, plus 8.5 percent of the profit over the annual goal."

"Done. I'll draw up the agreement and have it ready when I come to San Francisco. When will you be prepared with the report?"

"Well, because we have an agreement, I will give you a little preview of Brickman's inventory numbers. As I understand it, he doesn't have much free stock. But, I know he is desperate to keep the booking he has with Christian. I don't know by how much, but I overheard him talking with our head of production. As I understand it, there's not much extra crab."

If Seven Seas is actually short against the market, the message is different to Tongbang than if they are simply managing the numbers closely between anticipated supplies and bookings for future delivery, or if they had good supplies in inventory. Rookies get caught all the time — short on an up market, and long going down. What's worse is that they often get whipsawed in the middle, as they try to quickly jump to the other side of the trade to cut their losses. Pros like Brickman and Tongbang are always on the right side of the market. As long as the market is rising, they are in long positions. But if the market is topping, or worse, falling, they are always short.

Tongbang explains that he is traveling to San Francisco over the next weekend for a meeting. They decide to meet for lunch at the Golden Dragon in Chinatown on the following Monday.

Tongbang escorts her down to the lobby elevator, and as they walk, Jane probes him for details about the new company.

"We will have plenty of time to discuss the details after Monday. Just make sure you are ready. Enjoy your flight back."

The driver is waiting as Jane exits into the sunlight at the private entrance. The sun seems incredibly bright after the dusk of the warehouse interior, and Jane squints until she can find her sunglasses. Her eyes quickly adjust to the glare of the relentless Southern California sunlight as she climbs into the back of the car.

Walking back to his desk, Tongbang asks his assistant to get Lauren Hapides on the phone in Seattle, and follow that with a call to Arkady Gasparov in Vladivostok.

"Win, I don't know if I can wait until Monday. We've got Feds and Coast Guard all over the yard in Dutch. Nothing solid, but they are definitely looking for something."

"Lauren, you are getting too excited. Relax. I'm working on it. By tonight, this investigation will be over. Guaranteed. Meet me in the lobby of the Mandarin in San Francisco, as we agreed, at 10AM on Monday."

"Win, there's a copy of the construction specifications that was made after I changed the tonnage number on the boats. The back-ups are kept in our info technology and engineering offices in San Francisco."

"Lauren, when you get to San Francisco, go to the office and get the back-up copy, and bring it to me at the hotel. I will have my people here change the tonnage figures and have the copy back to you by lunch. Plan on meeting me at the Golden Dragon in Chinatown at Noon. Then you can return the back-up to the office files. You better make this right, You understand?"

Hapides has been under Tongbang's thumb ever since she was quietly dismissed by the Department of Commerce. He has leveraged her dismissal and his payoffs to get whatever information he wants from her whenever he wants it. She is in the habit of succumbing to his veiled threats to reveal her story to her employer and the industry, and she has become numb to the consequences of her actions, at least until the loss of the two boats. The deaths have finally shaken her to her senses. She now realizes that their relationship has taken her over the edge, and she is slowly coming to the realization that, regardless of the outcome, she will put an end to it, once and for all.

"But Win, how can I possibly do that? What will my excuse be for requesting the back-up tapes?"

"Lauren, I didn't say request them. You need to find a way to get them. Be careful. I think you should find a way to take care of this. Do you understand? You're getting money from me, aren't you? And you are protected, aren't you?"

After hanging up, Tongbang's assistant announces that Gasparov is waiting on the line.

"Win Tongbang, my friend. You must hurry. It is lunch time here, and they are holding the food for me."

"Arkady, there will be time for food. Now is for business. I want to know how many tons you can supply me for delivery in November. B-Grade only."

"Tongbang, my friend, we are beginning to run low here. The catch is poor, and Europe is crying for more product."

"Don't give me that bull shit, you old thief. You have nowhere to go with that B-Grade. I know that half of it won't pass the EEC[1] authorities. Now, I want your number, and I want your price, with a 72-hour hold until Monday, close of business, Pacific time."

"Actually, I will have a very tough time coming up with any volume. I mean it. But so I know what are you actually buying, tell me your volume and price, and I will see what is possible. You know better than me."

"I'll take one to two million pounds. And my price is $3.45."

"Are you mad?! Europe is paying that number in Euros!"

"Arkady, you heard me. $3.45. Make it happen."

1 European Economic Community

"What about the glaze? Same ten percent over glaze, 90 percent net weight?"

"Yes, same as before. Ten percent, no more," Tongbang agrees.

"But, you take possession FAS[2] Vladivostok. I want the letter of credit opened immediately with the usual arrangements for my office. You understand? I will confirm it tonight."

"I want to know now, or the deal is off."

"OK, OK. It's a deal. We will look for the letter tomorrow. *Svydanya*,[3] Mr. Win."

---

2 Freight Alongside Ship
3 Russian for Goodbye.

CHAPTER 36

Jane exits the limo at curb side, and is promptly greeted with the singing and spooling of titanium aircraft-engine blades. She's calmed and relieved by the sound of the thundering engines rolling out over the beach. There was something in the conversation with Tongbang that is gnawing at her. Even the smell of all of that money can't quite overpower the sense of dread about him — or the deal. Or . . . herself. She just can't seem to figure it out, or let it go — until now, that is. She is met at the curb and escorted to the private passenger lounge, where she approaches the concierge desk, checks in, and is then escorted to the waiting area, with its full bar.

"It's almost 4:30. Vodka rocks and a glass of club soda." The bartender motions at the Grey Goose, and Jane nods her approval.

She continues her thought process about Win Tongbang. Why did he call her now? And why did he offer company equity right off the bat? There wasn't even a conversation about employment. He must have known that I would never move for anything less than stock, especially if he knows anything about Brickman. Why, that prick. But still, what is the point of selling him out? Is there something to gain by causing trouble for Seven Seas? Tongbang made a point of the necessity of the position report, but that is proprietary information, and she has never done anything like that before. What is the purpose of doing it now? Unless he had a purpose? The report would give Tongbang detailed information on the inventory and pending orders for the largest king crab producer in the country. Why does he need it? What is the outcome he is looking for? Is he deceiving me?

"Jane?"

David Shepard steps around a bar stool and sits down, while motioning to the bartender to double the order. Dramatically eyeballing the lobby full of the rich and famous, "Looks like the tips I gave you have been paying off."

"David!" Jane spins up from the chair, and reaches out and hugs Shepard in a generous embrace. "Wow!" she says, letting him go.

He is as surprised at her response as she is. "What are the chances? I mean, I was just thinking about you. Well, sort of thinking about you. Not exactly the kind of place you'd expect to find a couple of salespeople, is it?"

"Frankly, I want all of my students traveling in private jets. What's a selling hour is worth today — 10, 20, $30,000 gross? Does it make any sense to have you tied up for hours hassling at LAX, or on a plane where you can't make a phone call or send an e-mail? Where's the ROI in that?"

"Right. Listen David, I'm so glad to see you. I need your help on a real problem."

"You have me for half an hour."

Jane proceeds to explain the details of the deal Win Tongbang has offered her, concluding with Tongbang's request that she provide him with the Seven Seas position statements.

"This isn't my wheelhouse, Jane. But I'm glad to ask you questions that may help you crystallize your options, or to simplify your decision. Your question isn't business-relational deal-making. It's personal. It's, well . . . it's ethical."

"I understand. I promise that I won't ask you for your judgment on the matter."

"Then here's my first question for you. What is your purpose? When it comes to your work, what really matters, and why is it important? What is your purpose?"

She's caught off guard, and begins scouring her internal RAM for the "correct" answer. Shepard detects that she is struggling with the question, and intervenes.

"Relax, Jane. There's no right answer to that question. There's only your answer, and it may take you some time to figure it out, especially if you haven't thought about it. But authentic, personal answers inform every business decision you make, especially when it comes to right and wrong. When your answers are authentic, you are coherent and energized. When they're not authentic, you're out of phase with your values. And that's when things can, and do, go wrong."

"Frankly, David, I don't have a good answer, and I'm not going to try to make one up. It's always about getting to the next income level, getting the promotion, winning the bigger customer."

"Yes, that's common among D-DISC types, which is why they hit the wall."

"Money, prestige, and achievement are huge motivators. You should never lose sight of their importance, or the amount that you value them. Hard work will assure that you keep the money flowing in. So, kudos for getting your ass out of bed in the morning."

"I'm glad to hear you say that, because I was beginning to think you were going soft on me."

"Not soft, just real."

"Look, I'm real. I deal with people every day, about millions of dollars in deals. It's business. It doesn't get more real than that."

Shepard pauses, then offers, "Here's the bad news. A simple twist of fate can take it all away. A situation, by the way, that can be completely out of your control."

Suddenly sobered, Jane flashes back to her TradeRaider bankruptcy, and his remark takes on an iron-cold clarity. "Fuck yes," she says under her breath.

"Unfortunately, when it does go away, you go with it. You're meaning as a person gets flushed away with it, and what's left in assets may be as thin as the values and relationships you have invested in over the years. If that account is empty, you may find that there's not enough to sustain you."

"David, I lost almost everything five years ago. There weren't too many who stood by me. Very few, but the list included Brickman."

"When it's something important to you personally, "in yer gut" — typically another person or other people — you'd better honor it. Here's my one piece of advice: Don't violate an important personal truth. Stand by those who stand by you."

At once, the picture clears, and she is baffled by why she had ever even considered Tongbang's request to steal the position statements. She understands that position reports are essential competitive information that could only benefit Tongbang Brothers, and could only hurt Ryan Brickman.

She slowly rotates her face towards Shepard from a chin-down position, pursing her lips and peering at him from the corners of her eyes. She pulls her chestnut hair carefully behind her left ear. With an imperceptible shaking of her head, she gives in, all at once, to the wisdom of his words.

Sensing that his work is done, Shepard knocks down the few remaining drops of alcohol in the bottom of his glass, snags a small ice cube with his tongue, and steps off the stool, crunching the ice as he speaks.

"I'm hitching a ride to Hong Kong with a client, then back to Australia. Shoot me an e-mail and let me know how things work out."

Jane stands and reaches out with a grateful embrace, thanking him for the guidance with an aura of newfound humility.

CHAPTER 37

"The Russians admit to having an old Typhoon-class sub shadowing the boats at 25 fathoms, goofing off and checking out the new hull designs. According to their naval attaché, the boats were paired up when the sub ran an emergency blow of its ballast." The Coast Guard's commanding admiral for the North Pacific had received an unexpected visit from the State Department's Naval Liaison for Eastern Europe.

"Our people figure 2,000 tons of water were ejected out and up underneath the two boats. Stupid frat-boy maneuver, but it shouldn't have capsized them. Not if they were seaworthy. But when your people found that the Plimsoll marks were wrong, and with the decks loaded with gear, it all made sense. The turbulence of the blow was enough to flip them. The poor bastards never had a chance. The sub took off, but the National Security Agency and the Naval Reconnaissance Office caught its echo signature at the scene by satellite and sent it to us. We then called the Russians.

"Admiral, I understand that you have a lot of people asking questions around here, but this one will never see the light of day. It can't. The State Department is not risking a beef with that gangster Putin over a couple of fishing boats, especially with such thin evidence."

"But what about our investigation? Word is out that the numbers were altered before we certified the boats. We've brought in a crime team. My people — and we aren't taking this fall — we . . ."

"Frank, if you dig any deeper, you're going to have the NSA and the State Department climbing up your ass. The investigation is over. Do you understand? We have people working on an official story. That kid they found in the engine room of the SIRIUS — Christian, I believe his name was — your folks tell us they suspect that he was murdered, based on the autopsy. Turns out he has a record in Denver for dealing cocaine and prescription drugs. They wiped it out when he agreed to turn on his suppliers. My people are working up a story that hangs the sabotage on his drug connection. It'll soon all be over with. The story will be leaked to the wires within 24 hours."

CHAPTER 38

With Shepard's words still echoing in her ears, Jane exits the CX hanger at SFO in the dark, and crosses the parking lot to her car. Before she starts the engine she punches the speed-dial button for Brickman's office phone, and closes her eyes to concentrate on exactly what she will say to him. Brickman punches the speaker phone on his desk as he receives a printout of Tokyo prices from Art Lesterman.

"Ryan, the mid-morning Tsukiji printout shows the A-Grade crab price down almost ¥210 per kilo. That's nearly a buck a pound. Looks like Watanabe is good to his word."

As Brickman gazes across the table at Lesterman, his eyes tighten, as if he is looking into a bright light. "And we're $20 million short, right? Jane where are you? I know I said the morning, but things are moving fast, can you get over here tonight? I want to start on the retailers by quietly rewriting the deals with Hoffman and Newday at two dollars below the contract price. That should put a smile on Carl Christian's face. Call Charlie Earlsfield in the London, and give him the same number. Then call the regional retailers who we aren't currently selling to, and give them offers of one dollar a pound under Tongbang's street price. Book any takers, and be prepared to drop the price a dime a day to anyone who asks for it. I want you to rewrite the deals with Hoffman, as well."

Molinari, Seven Seas' attorney, who's also in Brickman's office, jumps in. "Ryan, what about Robinson-Patman? You're talking about a dollar a pound difference between the price you are offering the large customers and the small customers. You need to offer the same deal to all customers."

" Forget it, Mike. The Feds never chase us on predatory pricing. You have to be one of the public companies, and even they can beat it. Listen Jane are you there?

"Yes I'm here."

"Just to be safe, don't put any offers on paper. Just tell them to send you the purchase orders in exchange for the firm quote. Make 'em think their getting in on something special."

Jane interrupts, "Ryan, I can't make it into town tonight, but I need to talk to you before we go any further. It's about our deal."

"Let's talk it over in the morning, Jane. There's too much going on right this minute. But I promise this time. I've got Mike right here in front of me and he's got the stock proposal."

"No Ryan, we need to talk right now."

Lesterman, his lanky frame slouched across the chair and table, turns to look at Molinari. "Ryan, I'm going to call for the latest numbers from Tsukiji. I'll be back in a couple of minutes."

"Jane, make this fast. I've got a lot on my mind."

"Win Tongbang flew me to San Diego today and offered me a partnership, under the condition that I deliver him the Seven Seas position statement on king crab."

Never one to guard his emotions, Jane has often seen Brickman fuming mad, near the point of violence, and she is prepared for the worst. But his reaction is beyond expectation. There is dead silence on the other end of the phone, and Brickman only responds after repeated appeals from Jane.

"What did he offer you?"

She recaps Tongbang's offer in sobering detail.

Brickman considers asking her why she hadn't taken the deal, why she is even talking with him right now. But, he already knows the answer.

"Ryan, I didn't say I wasn't taking the deal. I haven't decided yet. I've always thought that my future was Seven Seas. But it's not — not without ownership. And I'll take any deal that gets me to that position."

"When are you going to give him your answer?"

"No agreement on that. Whenever I turn over the report, I suppose, or soon thereafter."

Brickman looks across the desk at Molinari, who has been taking notes on the call. "Mike, I need you to redraw the Dreyfus deal by tomorrow to be equivalent to the TB offer. We need to get this done now. Can you do it?"

Molinari nods yes.

Jane interjects, "Ryan, listen, I'm not going to sign whatever you put in front of me. You know that, right? It needs to be better by ten percent."

"Not so fast, let's not get nervous, Kid." He turns to Molinari. "Same salary, plus five percent."

"Eight percent, Ryan!"

"Mike, make it 7.5 percent, and no more, Jane. That's it. Deal?"

"Let me look it over in the morning, but I agree in principle to the deal."

"I'll have Mike here by 11 o'clock so we can get this done on the spot after the crab meeting. We'll write it together if there are any discrepancies."

Lesterman, interrupts to announce that the Tokyo price has stabilized, and it seems to have reached a plateau, at least for the time being.

"Good. That's healthy. Means there are still players in the market who need to cover their positions." Brickman rubs is palms together. "Art, run a copy of the crab position report for Jane. She's going to send it down to Win Tongbang."

Jane's voice blurts out over the speaker system. "What?! Are you out of your mind?"

"Tongbang will read the report, and be convinced that the market is short. He'll keep buying the B-Grade from the Russians. By the time he and 'Stalin' wake up from their mutual gratification party, the Tokyo market will be off 20 percent."

☙

CODA

The global collapse of the king crab market eventually brings Tongbang Brothers to their knees, as the downward momentum eventually has them out-bidding their own prices.

Sensing the severity of the turmoil in Tokyo, Arkady Gasparov presents stacks of delivery documents drawn against Tongbang Brothers' Islandbanc letters of credit, and, without discrepancy, the documents are negotiated, and the cash is transferred. Enraged, Win Tongbang reveals to Russia's compliance committee that Gasparov had demanded a two percent kickback for his services in managing Russia's crab fishery. Gasparov's tenure as "Crab Czar" is brought to an abrupt end.

Ryan Brickman and Akiro Watanabe profit handsomely from their coordinated short — one of the greatest market manipulations in the history of the business.

Jane hangs up from the call with Brickman elated that apparently her partnership deal will finally be consummated, but only because Molinari is such a compulsive C-type, and she knows he will hold Brickman to his word, based on some rule of law about witnessed verbal contracts. The realization sinks in and she is suddenly euphoric.

Jane pulls out onto the 101 ramp north, pressing the accelerator slowly to the firewall as the Porsche upshifts to fifth gear. It is nearly midnight, and the four-lane is quiet, except for the tail lights of two trucks up ahead. They're on the outside of the curve that turns a few degrees north of northeast and into the city. Soon she is climbing the westbound ramp to I-280, and in minutes she has cleared El Camino as she heads south. This is always a favorite moment for her — the night ride on this perfect road home from the long trip and all that's behind her. Many uncertainties are now resolved. Business has been accomplished, and only a few lose ends are worth worrying about. As the speedometer climbs past 80, she's on speed memory through the events of the past seven days.

Brickman shipping her out, only to call her back because of the disaster in Dutch Harbor. Meeting David Shepard on the plane, and the amazing insights she has gleaned from their conversations about relationships and expectations. The meeting with Charlie Earlsfield, and his and Nigel Howard's focus on investigating the outcomes that are important to Hoffman-UK, while eliminating all of the typical vendor-centric marketing babble that means nothing to a prospect. The reality-testing questions that Charlie focused on as a way of getting to the truth and qualifying the prospect, rather than allowing the prospect to qualify him.

As the speedometer pegs toward 100, she suddenly experiences the tingling sensation of speed that always begins to fill her body, as the wind around the car takes on a different texture and quietness, as if it is airborne.

There were Shepard's instructions about remaining in control, and about the probability of winning, as long as she remained in control, and about never becoming so enthralled with a potential customer that she loses sight of the personal empowerment of exercising her rights to control the process as she saw fit.

There is an easy Zen perfection at speeds over 110. And it has become an addiction to Jane. The car speeds down the magnificent, elevated roadway, which is cut in, and mounted beautifully on, the wall from a scar of the San Andreas fault running miles below it. Then it's up onto the cantilevered and bridged segment that flattens and straightens the hills south of the city. Her record is 131, and climbing through 125 tonight she feels the relaxing rush of adrenaline that tells her she will easily blow past it.

And then there was the presentation, Shepard's instruction on maintaining the clarity of selling them back their dream, while going negative to uncover the impediments that always hide like an iceberg below the surface, just waiting to wreak havoc on even the most iron-clad agreement. The personal and physical attraction she had felt for Hella Elgar, and the lingering intoxication of being with Melina Bunge.

She will remember this trip for a very long time.

Finally, Win Tongbang's offer, and the timing of it all, with Brickman finally delivering on his promise — at least at this point, it appeared that he would. She feels redeemed and exhilarated, while instinctively pressing the accelerator deeper into the firewall.

The fence flanking the highway, put there to prevent wildlife from accessing the right of way, fails this time. At first glimpse, the animal leaps from the shoulder, at first startlingly fast, then in perfect super-slow motion. Hooves appear in the upper left-hand corner of the high-intensity beam from the car two lengths ahead. The racked head follows, barely aware of the impending disaster. Jane can see that the animal's right eye has already registered the doom. It has processed the data, and has resigned itself to fate.

The buck completely fills her Targa's windshield, and, though she pulls the wheel abruptly right to avoid it, the glancing blow shatters the safety glass windshield, beginning at the spot in the upper right-hand corner where an antler punched a hole, then spreading like bloody webbed lightening across to the driver's side. The car briefly lunges forward, then releases, and begins a flat, clockwise spin beneath her. All seems impossibly quiet, and both Jane's perceptions of her actions, and the sequencing of the events around her, become slow, as death itself, and with some uncanny purpose of design that she feels defenseless to alter. She struggles to pull the front of the front end back to the left, out of the 130-mph, sideways "whipper" down the empty highway. But the road is greased by the sheer speed, the diving angle, and the impossibly low-hanging center of gravity of the Porsche. As she pumps the wheel to the left, the car begins to gently lift up toward vertical. Then the hurricane-force wind puts the car in a rotisserie, rotating to the right. In a split-second, all control becomes conditional.

As the steering traction vanishes, it takes with it Jane's last shred of confidence in her power over a dark outcome tonight. She punches instinctively on the brake, as if she can stop the frames of the film, as if she can stop the events unfolding before her. But all control is gone, all lost, and at that instant she is present and aware that her physical survival is fully in the hands of the physics in chaotic certainty around her. Her mind is tuned to a crystal clarity, attendant with "Christ, I'm gonna die here."

The anticipation of that fills her with an altogether uncanny sensation — an almost child-like release of responsibility, of the need or the will to control it all.

As the car rotates 90 degrees, now opposed to the direction she was driving, the tire sidewalls compress under the wheel and the spinning magnesium begins grinding into the concrete surface, creating a blue-hot shower from under the wheel wells on passenger side. Jane can see them in a halo of light, as her head is tossed from forward to the right — beginning with the dazzling cobweb pattern that ignites across the crushed glass of the windshield and creates a kaleidoscopic display of the illuminations in front of the car. It even occurs to her as uncanny that in this horrific state, in this chaos within the car at this instant, she appears to be suspended in time. As the energy gradually transitions from linear to rotational, the car lifts Jane and begins spinning first on the axis of the drive shaft and after continuing to rotate and returning to the road surface begins to cartwheel end-over-end, beginning with the rear of the car. And with that comes a calmness to this particular 100th of a second that sweeps over her with comforting warmth. The warm waves well up through her entire body, flowing up from her feet and torso and into her face. She's become mildly aware that her skull has collided with the rearview mirror. Blood is spinning out of the gash in her forehead and into the weightless frame of reference. The car continues to hurtle through the damp Pacific air.

Her life has become entirely conditional. The control that was
part of the daily uniform proudly worn during every waking hour
has disappeared altogether. At the moment of the collision, reality
itself was transformed from granular, absolute control of velocity,
direction, plan, aspiration, and creation into a trivial variable with
a value going to zero. Her life at this moment is little more than
a physics experiment in kinetics. Control to condition. And it is
instantly clear to her this accident will not put an end to her. In
just that millisecond, there's a glint of awareness and a rise of a
smile across her face. Awareness of the ridiculous tyranny of fear
and uncertainty, and her angst over death and dying, is revealed
as just so much wasted time charged against one's mortality. Now
as it approaches, the inevitability brings an extraordinary and
fully present sensation of warm expectation — like a child feels
in the moments before the movie starts. Just another skating up
to the razors edge of reality, where she loved to visit, if not live.
Nothing spectacular or uncanny, just the good sense that the time
has arrived, and curious for the show to begin. She is completely
confident that even if this world should suddenly come to an end,
Jane Dreyfus was here forever.

The energy of the hurtling coupe distributes itself over all axes of
rotation such that the forward motion is slowed somewhat by the
spinning and pin-wheeling yawl. The car violently strikes concrete
again, and reverts to somersaulting. She observes it all in perfect
consciousness. Her neck snaps forward slowly as she watches her
hands passing by in the opposite direction, towards the headliner.
Between the 0.24- and 0.28-second mark her body is pressed
tightly against the seat back by the exploding air-bag, but just
as quickly it becomes nearly weightless yet confined by the seat
belts. She is vaguely aware that there is something wrong in the

pedal area at her feet. A piece of metal, perhaps the stem of the accelerator, has spiked like a gaff through the lower muscle of her calf above her Achilles tendon. With the car nearly vertical, she is, for the moment, dangling from it like a pig in a slaughterhouse, while blood from her forehead flows up into her scalp. As the front of the car rotates, the blue-white beam of the headlamps pan slowly down from skyward to illuminate the approaching concrete leg of an overpass. She watches in terrible fascination through the hole in the windshield like a child peeking between her fingers at the scary part of a horror movie. She is powerless to stop it. She closes her eyes and escapes.

Two great curtains stand in black and white before her. She looks back over her shoulder and sees the car, sees herself in the car, and turns away. Slowly the curtains draw apart, revealing a dazzling light and colors of variety and brilliance like she's never seen. She senses that she is a little girl now, standing at the entrance to a wonderful circus tent. It is a marvel, and they all those inside the tent know her. She doesn't want to, but she can't keep from looking back and watching the events unfolding behind her. It is dark behind her, but she can see the ambulance and the EMTs as they work to revive her. Oddly, the scene doesn't frighten or interest her in the least. She is only observing, and doesn't want to go back. But she is wondering why she's compelled to keep looking back again and again.

"Turn around, Jane," she tells herself. Those around her are inviting her to move on in a very warm and loving invitation. With each step she is deeper into the invitation and the light, as if each carries her faster and faster forward, and each time she turns back the image is more faded.

At once Jane begins sliding backwards. She reaches out to the others beyond the curtain — the ones who are leading her on, the ones who know her and understand. But she can not hold on to them. She tries holding onto the light, desperately reaching for that place within the light, but now it is moving away from her and spreading out faster and faster, and she is sliding backward and nothing she does can prevent it. At once she can see the EMTs again below her and she is fighting and becoming angry. Now she can barely see the light, and she is indignant.

She is screaming and swinging when she is suddenly seized by the pain in her leg. Like a crashing wave, she is struck by a vomiting, visceral pain originating from her leg and her skull that meets in the middle at her solar plexus. She lurches up into a blinding light, a different light, and the air is filled with the smell of gasoline and acrid, toasted latex.

· · · · · · ·

It's a beautiful spring evening 18 months later, and Jane crosses the pedestrain bridge from the airport into the garage. It's the end of an incredible road trip that has put to bed the most important set of deals of her career, and has lifted her business beyond the range of anything she ever imagined. Soon she will be off to Bangkok for the best part the deal — finalizing the sourcing side of the business with the P.O.s firmly in hand.

She reviews how powerful the Guess-Free Selling process has made her and the entire sales experience. She is now in control of her outcomes, and no longer gives any concern to issues beyond her control. Her job is collecting decisions and a single-minded focus on manifesting certainty. Employing purposeful reality-testing questions, she is producing wins with extraordinary predictability.

As she spins the wheels on the vintage red Carrera, she drops the shifter confidently into fifth and accelerates the engine up to 3500 rpm, lifting the car confidently up the cloverleaf and screaming across the flatlands toward the eastern flank of the Santa Cruz Mountains, toward Laguna Grande. The sun-dried southern zephyrs up from San Jose are failing with the light, and now and then the car submerges into a thick, chilling finger of fog that's stretching over the ridge to the southeast toward the runway. She punches the accelerator to the fire wall, and the wonderful acceleration drives up and forward as the wheels climb the soaring concrete ribbon, banking up and south toward home.

THE AUTHORS

DAVID DOUGLASS LIGHT

Dave's career spans his early days as a teamster on the
San Francisco waterfront to chemical production engineer, to
international trader, to national account lead, and to entrepreneur
and CEO. His sales travels have taken him to 21 countries on

sourcing and export-related
projects in business development
and leadership roles, while he
served an elite circle of national
customers. In 1991, Dave and his
family returned to their hometown
of Philadelphia from the Bay Area.

SCOTT MESSER

Scott's career as a business-
development professional and serial
entrepreneur spans more than 30
years. To Sales Evolution he brings
a blend of leadership, management,
and communications skills, along
with diverse experience in firms ranging from early-stage ventures
to large, established companies. He has built strategic alliances,
co-founded start-ups, overseen two mergers and acquisitions, and
built new business units. Originally from Pittsburgh, Scott now
lives in Philadelphia.